WITHDRAWN
Carleton College Library

THE EMIGRATIONS OF ANIMALS FROM THE SEA

The Emigrations of Animals From the Sea

A. S. PEARSE

Professor of Zoology

Duke University

THE SHERWOOD PRESS, PUBLISHERS
DRYDEN, N. Y.

PRINTED IN THE UNITED STATES OF AMERICA
BY THE MONUMENTAL PRINTING CO., BALTIMORE, MD.

PUBLISHER'S NOTE

This book is a natural outgrowth of Professor Pearse's book, "The Migrations of Animals from Sea to Land," published in a very limited edition in 1936 by the Duke University Press. Although much of the text remains the same, many additions and corrections have been made, the bibliographic references and the material have been brought up to date, and the illustrations added. Because of this, and the change in title which reflects a slightly different theme, it is felt that the book can hardly be called a second or a revised edition.

To

W. R. G. ATKINS

ACKNOWLEDGMENTS

IT IS a pleasure to acknowledge the help received from various sources in the preparation of this book. The Carnegie Institution through its Marine Biological Laboratory at Tortugas, Florida, furnished excellent facilities for work; the Director, Dr. W. H. Longley, and the Superintendent, Captain John Mills, did everything possible to help in the study of migration problems. Dr. A. V. Kidder and Dr. S. G. Morley made it possible to study the cenotes and caves in Yucatan; Don Carlos Vales, Gustav Stromsveck, and Karl Ruppert greatly facilitated the work in the field. The Rockefeller Foundation furnished funds and equipment which permitted the writer to make observations in China, Siam, India, and Nigeria. The following persons also materially assisted with the work in the localities indicated: Japan—Prof. N. Yatsu and Mr. N. Yosii, of the Misaki Biological Station, and Mr. S. Yoshimura, of the Imperial University of Tokyo; Dean T. Kitashima, Keio University; China—Prof. C. R. Kellogg, Pres. C. T. Lim, and other members of Fukien Christian University; Siam—Dr. H. M. Smith, Dr. Gordon Alexander, A. F. G. Kerr, A. Markan, E. D. Congdon, Nai Pongse Phintuyotsin, Siri Habanananda, Prof. Max Moller, and Luang Manjijjprasitte; India—Dr. R. B. Seymour-Sewell, Dr. S. L. Hora, Dr. Hem Sing Pruthi, and R. A. Hodgart, all of the Indian Museum, Calcutta; Nigeria—Dr. F. F. Russell, Dr. Henry Beewukes, and Rufus Gibson of the West African Yellow Fever Commission, and Dr. William Allen and F. A. Bemister, administrative officers of the Nigerian government. Dr. I. E. Gray has kindly read the manuscript for this book and made many helpful suggestions. My good friend Dr. Carl L. Hubbs made many valuable suggestions for changes from the 1936 book. Dr. R. H. Arnett, Jr., and Dr. R. E. Blackwelder also contributed photographs and made helpful suggestions.

A. S. P.

CONTENTS

THE EMIGRATIONS OF ANIMALS FROM THE SEA

1

INTRODUCTION

"We must interpret the present by the past" (Osborn, 1925).
"Science had to begin, not with problematical events from the past, but what actually happens before our own eyes" (Driesch, 1908).

PLANTS and animals cannot exist except in an environment. Those that dominate the earth today have struggled up a long evolutionary trail from the past. They perhaps began, when the earth was hot and even more or less molten, as inorganic substances in which carbon, nitrogen, oxygen, hydrogen, sulphur, iron, and other elements were combining to form such compounds as cyanide (Pflüger, 1875), water, carbon dioxide, ammonia, and acetylene. As the earth cooled, acetaldehyde, aldol, crotonic acid, and possibly even amino-acids formed (Kraft, 1931). At a certain stage in evolution when the environment had attained a stability which somewhat resembled the conditions that prevail today, there came into existence protoplasmic, metabolic, self-sustaining, and self-perpetuating organisms. Once established, organisms began their evolution. As environments varied, many organisms became extinct. A few gradually progressed in complexity and ability and now dominate the earth. Today certain earth animals are able to sit in stable, automatically regulated environments that they have themselves made, and write treatises on the problems of science. Yet even proud man carries his heritage from the past. His blood plasma has been called archaic sea water; during his embryological development piscines gill arches appear on the sides of his neck-to-be; in adult life his bifocal vision and prehensile limbs remind him of ages long gone by when his ancestors lived in trees.

The characteristics of fossils indicate the nature of the environment in which the animals that formed them lived (Hubbard & Wilder, 1930). The great steps in evolutionary progress appear to have occurred when plants or animals surmounted the greatest environmental obstacles to invade new types of habitats where new earth resources could be utilized—when organisms left the ocean to take up life in fresh water and when they left the water for the land. This book is devoted chiefly to the consideration of such emigrations.

Since early geological eras the composition of the ocean has changed. There was formerly less salt. At present sodium and magnesium are slowly increasing, but calcium and potassium are practically stationary. Calcium is continually added to and is continually precipitated out of sea water. The development of vegetation and soils on land has retarded the movement of potassium to the sea. "Briefly animal as well as vegetable protoplasm owes its relation to the elements sodium, potassium, calcium, and magnesium, to the composition of sea water which obtained when all forms were unicellular, just as the blood plasma owes its relations to the same four elements to the composition of sea water when prevailing circulating fluids were established. In other words, the relation of protoplasm to salts is due to the action of sea water, for incalculably long periods of time on the living matter of unicellular organisms" (Macallum, 1904). In particular areas at various times in the past there have been considerable changes in sea level. "Although the slow widespread rise and fall of the sea surface have produced important geological results, yet the existing raised beaches and the upward growth of coral reefs into atolls are due to local variations in level of land, and not to general rise and fall of the sea" (Gregory, 1931).

Origin of Life

The origin of life remains a mystery. The only generalization based on evidence that biology has been able to make since the old, crude notions of spontaneous generation were disproved in the nineteenth century is "all life from life." Yet scientists have not been backward in proposing theories. Snyder (1909, 1911) believes that life was at first anaerobic and gives the following as his arguments: (1) many of the simplest organisms are today anaerobic; (2) fundamental cell processes are anaerobic, and oxidation is perhaps to be looked upon as only secondarily associated with life processes as a means of removing wastes; (3) aerobic life evolved from anaerobic because of increased need for oxygen; (4) the need for oxygen increases with increase in body size; and (5) the oxygen in the atmosphere has come largely from the activities of plants and was not present in considerable amounts until plants had evolved to such a degree that they could manufacture it. Snyder also discusses the physical conditions which he believes were associated with the beginnings of life. He postulates such a sequence of activities as: (1) reactions of carbon dioxide and water vapor in a concentrated mixture under the influence of electrical discharges to produce formaldehyde or even formic acid; (2) the reaction of such compounds with ammonia or with amine or imine radicals, or with prussic acid to form simple amino acids; (3) the precipitation of colloidal substances in a solution containing metal salts, such as those of phosphoric acid, and resulting combinations; (4) coagulations, resolutions, and aggregations of particles; and (5) "the formation, through the chemical activity of these bioblasts, of an enclosing membrane, resulting in the first living 'cells'." Crile, Glasser, Telkes, & Rowland (1932) emphasize the formation and activities of nitrocarbons as a primary quality of life. Gulick (1948) gives evidence from the point of view of a biochemist that supports his belief that life originated in the sea.

Donnan (1929) is convinced that the energy transformations of living cells conform with the first and second laws of thermodynamics,* but believes that the mechanism for the harmonious coordination of organs and tissues is still a mystery. Pike (1929) grants that the first law of thermodynamics clearly applies to organisms but asserts that some doubt may exist about the second. However, he concludes that the second law does apply and that the entrance of sunlight into plants and its utilization as a source of energy are spontaneous processes. Life on the earth depends on radiant energy from the sun. The origin of life Pike believes to be associated with the appearance of certain carbon compounds which are capable of yielding energy at certain stages in stellar evolution. Oxidative processes are spontaneous and drive organisms on to increasing complexity. "The arrest of energy degradation in living nature is indeed a primary biological concept. Related to it, and of equal importance, is the concept of organization" (Hopkins, 1933).

Many thoughtful persons who have discussed the origin of life believe that organisms first came into existence in the sea. Rogers (1928) points out that living things must have originated when the temperature of the earth was between the freezing point of water and the coagulating point of proteins, when short wave lengths of light were more abundant than at present. He believes that colloidal particles in water were bombarded and that, associated with adsorption on colloidal interfaces, simple compounds of carbon, oxygen, hydrogen, and nitrogen were built up. In such a simple system phosphorus, sulphur, iron, and other elements were included. A catalyst of simple type helped the early colloid to become an energy transformer. Chlorophyll, though complex, is such a substance. Rogers believes that there was not one origin, but that

*First Law: When mechanical work is transformed into heat or heat into work, the amount of work is always equivalent to the quantity of heat.

Second Law: It is impossible by any continuous self-sustaining process for heat to be transferred from a colder to a hotter body.

living matter came into existence many times, probably always in the sea where there was appropriate temperature and when the sea water was more dilute than now. Allen (1923) also maintains that life arose in the sea and stresses the importance of photocatalysts acting on water, carbon dioxide, and simple compounds of nitrogen. Richardson (1928) pictures the origin of life in tropical intertidal pools along rocky seashores, and emphasizes colloids and pigments as factors. Flattely & Walton (1922) say "the shore has strong claims to be recognized as the birthplace of life," and cite the littoral region as "the cradle of evolution."

Woodruff (Barrell *et al.*, 1924) has reviewed various theories of the origin of life.

The Sea as the Original Home of Life

In the oldest strata of sedimentary rocks which contain fossils the remains of plants and animals all appear to be marine. This indicates that life immediately before that time probably existed largely or wholly in the ocean. This of course does not preclude the possibility that life previously existed on land or in fresh water and became extinct without leaving records as fossils. However, "at the very begining of the Paleozoic Era are found all of the main kinds of marine animals other than fishes" (Schuchert, in Barrell *et al.*, 1924). The invertebrates had been in existence during the preceding eras (Archeozoic, Proterozoic) long enough for the chief types as they exist at present to become established. As time went on many of the older types (trilobites, etc.) became completely extinct and new types (chordates, etc.) came into existence. As evolution progressed, certain animals that were related to early chordates (ostracoderms, arthrodires, etc.) and some that were clearly chordate (cyclostomes, elasmobranchs) appeared in the ocean, but most of them and the bony fishes apparently had their origin in fresh water (Barrell, 1916; Noble, 1931; Bigelow, 1931; Romer, 1945).

The blood of all animals is saline. Many invertebrate animals that live in the sea have bloods which contain the same salts in the same proportions as those that are present in the surrounding medium. But the bloods of marine elasmobranch and bony fishes differ in salinity from sea water, the salt content being considerably lower. The bloods of fresh-water and land animals also contain less salt than those of marine invertebrates (Pearse, 1932b). Sea water is a medium which contains all the elements which are necessary for building and maintaining protoplasm. The general similarity of the bloods of animals to sea water has been interpreted as indicating that all animals originated in the sea. To explain qualitative and quantitative differences which exist between the salts in the bloods of both marine and non-marine animals and sea water, some have assumed that blood salinities in certain cases became established and stabilized long ago when the salts in the ocean differed in amount from those which are characteristic today. Such questions will be discussed more fully in Chapter 4. While there are many discrepancies to be explained, it is a common belief that "blood is modified sea water" (Pantin, 1931).

The life histories and breeding habits of certain types of animals indicate that they originated in the ocean and subsequently migrated to land. For example, crabs and hermit crabs which live in the ocean generally pass through characteristic swimming larval stages; certain land crustaceans of the same types spend most of their lives on land but return to the ocean once each year and leave their young for a short sojourn in their ancestral home. The larvae which thus require a marine existence are quite like those of crabs which never leave the sea. On the Irish coast three species of the same genus of shore snails are arranged in zones. The snails of the species that is found at low tide lay eggs which hatch into swimming veliger larvae, and these spend some time in the sea; those that live in the middle zone of the tidal area spend less time as swimmers;

those that live near high-tide mark pass through their swimming stages before hatching from the egg and never swim. Such a series is believed to indicate origin in the ocean and varying degrees of adjustment to life on land (Colgan, 1910). Bony fishes appear to have originated in fresh water, and many of them breed there. Altogether considerable evidence from life histories and embryological development indicates that a number of types of animals originated in the ocean and gradually invaded fresh-water and land habitats. The presence of gill arches in land vertebrates (reptiles, birds, mammals) during embryonic development means that such animals came more or less remotely from aquatic ancestors.

While it is generally admitted by most zoologists that life probably originated in the ocean, there is much difference of opinion as to the exact region where it appeared first. There are some (Brooks, 1894) who believe that life first came into existence in the open sea, but most authorities (Simroth, 1891; Osborn, 1917; Johnstone, 1908) do not favor such a view, largely because there is a paucity of available nitrogen compounds there. Manifestly the lack of nitrogen, light, and other favorable conditions does not make it seem probable that life began in the depths of the ocean. Life is generally believed to have originated in the littoral region.

Apparently no great groups (phyla) of animals originated except in the ocean (Hesse, 1920). The routes by which animals probably left the ocean and reached fresh water and land have been various. Some animals probably migrated directly across sea beaches; others probably ascended rivers, passed through marshes and swamps, or burrowed through soil. Some animals were transferred from the ocean by land elevations which isolated them in bodies of water which gradually became fresh. The ways animals followed from sea to land will be discussed in the next chapter.

Emigration from the sea did not take place at any one time. It has occurred many times in the past and is slowly progressing on many shores today. Among all types of animals there is a continual tendency to spread into new available habitats in order to escape interspecific competition. The most successful animal colonizers of the land have been: (1) the arthropods, which have in many cases developed book-lungs or tracheae for breathing air; (2) the vertebrates, with lungs and dry skins; and (3) the snails, with slime and spirally coiled shells to prevent desiccation. Certain burrowing worms and many amphibians, which have little ability to conserve water within their bodies, are struggling to maintain themselves on land, and under favorable conditions some of these have even taken up life in trees. There are at present many examples of animals which are in the midst of their transformation from marine to fresh-water animals, or from marine or fresh-water into land animals.

Not only have plants and animals emigrated from sea to land, but there are countless instances where migrations have taken, and are taking, place in the opposite direction. Grasses, insects, reptiles, birds, and mammals have left the land for the sea (Lull, 1917; Pearse, 1932e). In general, primitive plants (Bews, 1923) and animals (Kennedy, 1928) have remained in primitive habitats, but after secondary migrations such relations may become mixed. Emigrations from water to land perhaps take place most readily in moist situations in the tropics (Harms, 1929).

Clark (1927) disagrees somewhat with current opinion concerning the origin of life in the ocean. He says: "The fauna of the sea is the aquatic fringe of the fauna of land waters, which were more extensive in the geologic past than now; the sea itself is practically sterile. Life is most abundant on the land where there is the maximum water vapor in the air as in the moist tropics; it is most varied where conditions are varied. . . . Life probably arose in marshy water (non- or slightly saline)." Against the view that life originated in the ocean, Macfarlane (1918) argues that many primitive types of plants and animals occur today in fresh water. He states

(p. 502) that "such a trend of evolutionary progress does away entirely with a marine ancestry at any stage in the process." Chamberlain & Salisbury (1905) also believe that the first life consisted of plants and animals in "land waters" and that the latter "spread thence to the sea and out upon the land." Gilsen (1947) believes that animals originally invaded land from brackish or fresh-water coasts. Carl Hubbs in a letter says, "changing environment as a stimulus to evolution favors the view that most evolution took place in fresh water."

The geologic history of the earth and paleontologic history of plants and animals show that climatic changes have been rhythmical. Plants preceded animals on land (Case, 1919) and furnished basic food supplies. Land plants appear to have come from green algae (Bower, 1929), probably by direct migration from the ocean (Church, 1919, 1921, 1926). At first algae were probably pelagic, then sessile, and finally terrestrial. The reproductive organs of specialized plants did not come from those of bryophytes but from algae (Church, 1926). Pollen permitted fertilization out of water (Bower, 1929; Campbell, 1930), and seeds furnished nutritious, concentrated food (Berry, 1920). At the beginnings and ends of epochs there were striking changes in climate which preceded marked readjustments and evolutionary changes in animals. Deformation of the earth's crust, volcanic dust, and variations in the amount of carbon dioxide in the atmosphere were important factors in producing climatic changes (Case, 1919). A monotonous environment may permit many individuals to exist but limits the number of types; whereas a changing environment is associated with variety and the evolution of new types (Clark, 1925). "Nothing is better established, amidst all the confusion of the discussions as to method of evolution, than the fact that the environment changes before changes appear in organic forms" (Case, 1926). On the other hand some animals are preadapted for certain new habitats

and readily enter them. For example, nematodes have an impervious cuticular covering and this permits certain of them to enter plants or animals as parasites.

Comparison of Ocean, Fresh Water, and Land

"*Das Land ist das Reich der Gegensätze, das Wasser das Reich des Gleichmasses*" (Simroth, 1891). Water habitats in general are more or less stable; land habitats as a rule present extreme variability. An animal that lives in water is in no danger of death by loss of water from its body fluids, but may be easily killed by soluble poisons in the surrounding medium. Water is comparatively stable because it absorbs and loses heat slowly and cannot circulate rapidly. Shallow water may be subject to violent wave motions, and small stagnant bodies of water may be deficient in oxygen. Land animals have a dependable oxygen supply. The land is subject to wind storms and to sudden and extreme changes in atmospheric temperature and moisture. As water is a dense medium compared to air, aquatic animals move slowly, while land animals may be speedy.

The ocean is in general more stable and uniform than bodies of fresh water because of its vast extent. Its high and varied salt content and relatively uniform temperature make it a favorable medium for protoplasmic activity. It is comparatively simple as an environment for plants and animals (Bigelow, 1931). It contains no nitrifying organims except near shore. A wide variety of algae are present in the sea, but only about thirty species of spermatophytes occur (Buxton, 1926). All phyla of animals are represented in the ocean; echinoderms, brachiopods, and tunicates are found

Fig. 1. Pool that has been cut off from the ocean at Dry Tortugas and is gradually growing less saline. (From Pearse, 1932e.)

nowhere else. A considerable number of types of animals which had their origin in, or became adjusted to life in, fresh water or on land have entered the ocean. Fishes began in fresh water but now range through the ocean at all depths. Many extinct and modern reptiles took up life in the ocean. Whales, pinnipeds, and certain birds, like the albatross and penguin, are truly oceanic, though their ancestors probably lived on land. Though insects are ubiquitous, aggressive, and dominant in many situations on land and occur in considerable numbers in fresh water, they have invaded the ocean very little. Alongshore are a few flies, midges, beetles, and apterous insects. Water striders run over the surface of the ocean in warm climates. Only one species of insect (a crane-fly) is submarine at all stages of its life cycle (Buxton, 1926; Tokunaga, 1930). However, if a pond is cut off from the ocean and becomes to some degree fresh, it is speedily invaded by insects—Diptera, Coleoptera, Odonata, Hemiptera, etc. (Pearse, 1932e). Cold sea water is more productive of life than that near the equator, perhaps because more trihydrol and oxygen are present in it or because conditions for nitrification and denitrification are more favorable. Trihydrol as colloidal water particles perhaps has a catalytic effect which favors the growth of aquatic organisms (Barnes, 1932a).

Although there is more than twice as much water as land surface on the earth (Fowler, 1928), the fresh-water areas of the world are isolated and limited in extent. Even the great lakes in Africa and North America are minute compared with the ocean. Fresh water is often variable in amount, as in swamps and rivers; is often subject to considerable variations in temperature, daily and seasonal, as in pools; and in various situations there may be wide differences in organic and inorganic content and reaction. In a shallow, stagnant pond or swamp where the surface is covered thickly with floating vegetation there may be no oxygen in the water at night. Such a condition is especially characteristic in the tropics. In eutrophic

Fig. 2. Arbuckle Creek, Florida, choked with water hyacinths so that there is little or no oxygen in the water below. (Photo by R. H. Arnett, Jr.)

lakes the deeper waters may be without oxygen for months at a time. Notwithstanding the severity of the conditions of life in fresh water most of the phyla that began life in the ocean have also become established there, but there is usually less variety. Certain rather modern families (*Astacidae, Limnaeidae,* etc.), orders, and even classes (Amphibia) are characteristic of fresh water, and do not often occur in the ocean.

Land plants and animals receive much energy directly from the sun and in the atmosphere have a dependable supply of oxygen, but they are frequently in danger of death by loss of water and must endure extreme fluctuations in temperature. Turbellarians, oligochaetes, polychaetes, onychophorans, myriapods, crustaceans, insects, arachnids, gastropods, and vertebrates are well established as land animals. Some of these are still obliged to live in moist situations, but such well-adapted types as certain snails, arachnids, insects, reptiles, birds, and mammals can exist even in deserts. Certain of the animals that have attained land life are of primitive marine stocks (Harms, 1929), but most successful land animals are modern, progressive types with impervious integuments and mechanisms for conserving water while breathing air.

In the four succeeding chapters the emigrations of animals from sea to land will be considered in some detail: the routes the emigrants followed; the reasons why animals left the dependable, stable ocean for a precarious life on land; the changes that have taken place in structures and functions of the animals that have succeeded in adjusting their systems of activities to land life; and the rewards that accrue to those animals that have struggled up long difficult trails and now view the world from mountain peaks. This has been the greatest emigration the world has known.

2

ROUTES FROM THE SEA

PLANTS and animals that have left the ocean to dwell on land or in fresh water have been obliged to acquire new ranges of toleration to certain environmental factors. They have done this chiefly where environment permitted experimental trials without death. On ocean beaches, in estuaries, in marshes and swamps, in temporary pools, in isolated bodies of water in which salinity changes slowly, in soil where sudden changes in temperature are not possible and where desiccation is inhibited, and in a few other situations organisms are ever striving not only to continue to live but also if possible to spread into new types of habitats in which they have not lived before. Migrations from one realm to another commonly take place along the borderlines of territories, where there are more or less gradual or intermittent changes in environmental factors. No pelagic marine animal has ever been transformed into a land animal.

Beaches

On the beaches along the seashore the ebb and flow of the tides brings about a rhythmical change in water level, temperature, and other conditions of environment. Currents and waves transport and beat upon plants and animals and may bring about changes in salinity over a particular area. Plants and animals that live on ocean beaches, attached to the bare faces of rocks, safely ensconced in crevices or burrows, in rock pools, or even swimming in the littoral

waters, live more or less both in air and in water. Marine animals thus have opportunity to become adjusted to life on land, and land animals may gain some ability to endure life under water. Many thoughtful, beach-haunting biologists have suggested ocean shores as one route through which old marine stocks of animals have reached land (Flattely, 1920, 1921).

The moving littoral water contains myriads of small organisms which serve as food for animals. The accumulations which have been left along the drift line above high-tide mark furnish food and shelter for both terrestrial and aquatic animals. There is keen competition for places to live between tide marks. The plants and animals on beaches are arranged in zones. Various factors contribute to enforce such zonal arrangement: the height of tides, the slope of the beach, the character of the bottom, etc. On most beaches zones are clearly defined by characteristic littoral plants. These in turn furnish protection and food for animals. At one locality on Long Island, N. Y., for example, there are about five zones of plants: (1) the plankton (peridinians, diatoms, etc.) in the littoral water, (2) the attached bottom vegetation (Ulva, Enteromorpha, Fucus, Chondrus, etc.), (3) a mid-littoral belt (Spartina, Fucus, Ascophyllum, Bostrichia, etc.), (4) an upper littoral belt which has rather varied vegetation (Spartina, Scirpus, Salicornia, filamentous algae, etc.), and (5) supra-littoral belt containing a great variety of plants (Johnson & York, 1915). Similar zonal arrangement of animals is characteristic on all ocean beaches (Harms, 1929; Huntsman, 1918a; Pearse, 1914, 1914a, 1929, 1931;

Fig. 3. Zones on a rocky shore at Nahant, Mass. From above downward: Barnacles, and the algae Ascophyllum, Fucus, and Chondrus. (From Pearse 1914.)

Verwey, 1930). It is apparent along the borders of coral reefs (Stephenson, Stephenson, Handy, & Spender, 1931) and also along those of fresh-water lakes (Forel, 1892-1904; Muttkowski, 1918).

Migration from aquatic to land habitats takes place most readily when the atmosphere alongshore is humid (Harms, 1929; Lusk, 1917). The height which marine animals attain on beaches is more or less directly related to humidity (Fischer, 1927). Animals that have taken up life on land have variable degrees of adjustment to atmospheric humidity. Some absorb water; others lose water at all temperatures, even when the air is saturated. Some animals become dormant in low humidities; others are active at night (Ludwig, 1945). On rocky shores marine crabs scamper in and out of the ocean most often at night, during rains, or when spray dashes high. In crevices animals can live higher than on exposed rock surfaces, because they are somewhat sheltered from wave action and desiccation. Along muddy beaches crabs and fishes wander into the adjacent land vegetation and often dodge into burrows. On clay and sand beaches animals commonly live in burrows and emerge only when humidity is favorable.

Air-breathing animals which take up residence between tides must migrate inshore at intervals or be able to endure submergence for several hours. Littoral mites can live for a couple of days under water (King, 1914). Intertidal insects have air stored in their tracheae, but also take advantage of small quantities of air which remain in crevices when the tide covers the beach.

On rocky coasts there are few or no plants at high-tide mark, but barnacles often occur in great numbers (Allee, 1923, 1923a; Pearse, 1914, 1929, 1931). Some rock barnacles are so situated that they are not covered by water except during the highest tides, which do not occur every day. A barnacle is typical of rock-beach animals—firmly attached; protected by a heavy calcareous covering against desiccation, extreme changes in temperature, and the pounding of waves; radial in symmetry and conical, so that waves easily slide over it; and adapted to catching food from water by spreading tiny, appendicular nets. A barnacle has long been used as an example of "retrogressive metamorphosis." During successive molts it changes from a free-swimming, appreciative (in that it has rather elaborate sense organs), and active animal to one that is unappreciative, sessile, and enduring rather than thoughtful. Such an animal as a barnacle gives no promise of producing a land animal in the future. Its habits and inheritance make it psychologically unprogressive. The same is true of many other typical beach animals.

Sessile littoral animals have not become terrestrial (Harms, 1929; Pearse, 1922), yet there are a few of the active animals, such as certain crustaceans and snails, that apparently have progressed directly across sea beaches to land. At Tortugas the ability of a variety of littoral animals to live in the atmosphere and in various dilutions of sea water was tested. Most of the animals lived longer in the air than in the water. This suggests that they showed little tendency to migrate to land by first becoming adjusted to fresh water (Pearse, 1929). As has been stated, certain land crustaceans go directly to the ocean to breed each year. Cannon (1923) studied the development of the eggs of a land crab, *Cardisoma armatum* Herklots, in various solutions. He found that all eggs hatched in sea water; a few hatched in half fresh and half sea water; and all died in fresh water. Algae high up on beaches are more resistant to desiccation than those which live in lower zones and grow more slowly; snails at higher levels show greater negative geotropism and positive phototropism than those below (Colman, 1933). There are many evidences that animals have passed directly, but of course slowly, from ocean to land.

The little pools which are left between tide marks when the ocean periodically recedes serve as refuges for some marine animals and for some which are partially adjusted to life on land. The pools low down on a beach are less exposed to sun, wind, rain, trickling springs, and other aboceanic factors and maintain more constant temperatures than those which occur at higher levels. Animals which are characteristic of the former are on the whole more stenothermic than those in the latter (Klugh, 1921). Sometimes, after rains or along shores where springs seep out over tide pools, a curious condition is established. A pool may be separated into a fresh-water stratum above and a salty, marine stratum below. The pool may therefore be inhabited by certain aquatic insects, worms, and other fresh-water animals living above the crabs, anemones, and other animals belonging to the ocean (Gersbacher & Denison, 1930; Pearse, 1914).

An ocean beach is a difficult place to live. There are low and high temperatures, strong tides, waves, desiccation, enemies which come inshore when the tide rises or run down from the land when the tide ebbs. Yet an abundant and varied fauna lives on ocean beaches. Advantages in the way of light, food, and oxygen apparently compensate for the disadvantages. Under the highly variable conditions on the beaches some animals, such as certain crabs and fishes, have undoubtedly become adapted to terrestrial existence. On the California coast, MacGinitie (1935) found most animals progressing toward land "through the surf, and not through estuaries."

Estuaries

Many types of animals have entered fresh water through estuaries. These have perhaps come in part from the "mudline" which borders every continental shelf just beyond the limits of wave motion. "From the general character of fresh-water species and from the almost complete absence of free-swimming larvae, we may suppose that the fresh-water fauna has also been derived from mud-line animals which ascended from the mouths of great rivers and from estuaries" (Murray, 1895). Annandale (1922) maintains that a large proportion of the animals which leave the ocean to live in fresh and brackish water are primitive types which have been unable to compete with more progressive marine animals. He looks upon estuaries as "a refuge for spent races." In the Ganges Delta he found that most of the animals in fresh and brackish tidal waters were marine in their affinities, but few such animals were to be found in the river above. Annandale was impressed by the continual pressure to enter new habitats which animals displayed, and surprised that so few marine species were able to establish themselves in the Ganges River. He affirmed that the attempts to invade fresh water were not anadromous or seasonal migrations but manifestations of a general tendency to spread. Pelseneer (1906) long ago expressed the view that river animals not only arose where temperatures were uniformly high, throughout the tropics, but also where the ocean was diluted by heavy rains. He cited Indo-China and the Bay of Bengal as a region which was particularly favorable for the transformation of marine into fresh-water animals.

Any stream is subject to change in volume and level. The Amazon River may rise 12 to 50 feet during the rainy season. The Nile periodically overflows the bottom lands along its banks, and the Egyptians have long correlated their agricultural activities with its rise and fall. Some small streams are intermittent. Their beds are actually dry at certain seasons. The instability which is associated with variations in volume, speed, and level of stream waters is probably not of particular significance in relation to the migrations of marine animals into estuaries, for there is always a stratification of waters in the mouth of a river which empties into the sea. The fresh, usually warmer, water flows over the denser saline water from the ocean. Marine animals may therefore live in the deeper parts of a river without being in fresh water. There is also more or less conflict between tide and river current. When the tide flows, salt water may invade the mouth of a river, especially when a favorable wind drives the surface water upstream, but under ordinary conditions the surface of a river is fresh, even for some distance out into the ocean beyond the mouth. The yellow waters of certain of the great rivers which flow eastward along the coast of China give approaching vessels notice of their presence before land can be seen. The estuary of a river which flows into a sheltered bay or sound usually shows a graded series of salinities, often with extensive areas of brackish water which may remain relatively constant. Bourn (Weese, 1928) on the Atlantic coast of the United States studied salinities at 26 stations in a brackish-water area. He says: "There is no correlation between salinity and the rainfall. . . . Since there are no meteorological tides in these inland waters, the salt content of Back Bay and Currituck Sound is governed by the force and direction of the winds. The influx of salt water in varying amounts has disturbed natural conditions and consequently, has greatly altered the aquatic life of the region."

In some respects, marine animals which burrow have a better chance to become adjusted to life in estuaries than those which live in the water above. "The water retained in the muddy foreshore of an estuary at low tide was more saline than the estuary water itself at the same distance from the sea. The retention of salt by the bottom and shore deposits may be a factor favoring the growth of burrowing animals in the central part of an estuary" (Alexander,

Fig. 4. Mangroves (Avacinea) in a Colombian estuary. The mud in which they grow contains little or no oxygen and many breathing roots grow up into the air. The small tree in the left foreground shows prop roots.

Southgate, & Bassindale, 1932). But Fraser (1932) at the mouth of the Mersey River found the clam, *Mya arenaria,* only where sand and gravel were mixed with mud. "Mud of a very liquid nature apparently contains no fauna."

Suspended materials are constant factors which influence the lives of animals at the mouths of rivers. Estuarine animals often show special adaptations which enable them to live in water which is heavily charged with silt. Sessile animals must grow in length to rise above accumulating sedimentary deposits. Robson (1925) states that the frontal width of an estuarine crab (Carcinas) decreases as water becomes more silty. Some estuarine species lack eyes; certain crustaceans are colored like their relatives in the deep sea, which also live on soft, muddy bottoms. River waters generally contain more organic matter per unit of volume than the neighboring ocean (Johnstone, 1908). Some estuarine animals, such as oysters, depend for a considerable portion of their food on small organisms carried in flowing water.

About the mouths of many streams in the tropics there are extensive growths of mangroves. Such areas are particularly favorable for various animals, which find food, shelter, and suitable conditions for reproduction among the aerial roots and branches of these peculiar plants. Though the mud in mangrove marshes is usually soft and without oxygen, the plants furnish strata which are occupied by a variety of animals. Mangroves are not xerophytes, as are many plants which are found in salt or brackish water. They have a thicker epidermis in salt water; some species excrete salt through the leaves and are thus able to absorb salty water without raising the concentration in their tissues. In many ways mangroves are adapted for life on the soft muddy bottoms of estuaries.

Altogether, an estuary is usually a region where, though there may be wide variations in environmental factors, there are more or less extensive areas where marine, fresh-water, or brackish-water animals may find favorable conditions for existence. At times curious associations of animals from various sources are found. Crayfishes and sunfishes may consort with swimming crabs; dolphins and king crabs live with river turtles and fresh-water snails.

Working in two such widely separated estuaries as those of the Ganges and the Thames, Annandale (1922) and Robson (1925) are in general agreement concerning the origins and characteristics of estuarine animals. Annandale points out that the fresh-water fauna of the world is quite cosmopolitan. The limnaeid and viviparid snails were already established in Cretaceous times. Animals of marine origin were present in the rivers of South America, Australia, China, India, and other regions. The Ganges River originated in the Tertiary Age. In its upper waters there are no marine animals in the "highly specialized fauna," but in the lower 900 miles there are four types which constitute the "relict fauna": (1) the dolphin, *Platanista gangetica* Lebeck, which does not leave the river, and is comparable to similar fluviatile dolphins in the Amazon and Yangtse rivers; (2) several species of the genus Naviculina, rather primitive clams belonging to the family *Solenidae;* (3) *Scaphula celox* W. H. Benson and *S. deltae* Blanford, clams; and *Ampelisca pusilla* Sars, an amphipod which also occurs in the Arctic Ocean. The euryhaline fauna of the Ganges delta includes: sponges, a fresh-water species and a boring one on shells; coelenterates, three widely distributed genera of hydroids and various species locally; polychaetes; an echiuroid; many snails and clams; several species of bryozoans; a king crab, *Carcinoscorpius rotundicauda* (Latreille), which has been seen in fresh water at Calcutta; various crustaceans, including amphipods, mysidaceans, shrimps, prawns, and crabs; fishes, anadromous, euryhaline, and estuarine; and a cetacean, *Orcacella brevirostris* Owen. There are few marine species in the river proper but many in the delta. "I cannot, however, find any definite dividing line between these two faunas. The relict fauna consists merely of organisms that have proved more capable of establishing themselves in abnormal circumstances and, therefore, more successful in the peculiar line of life adapted to them." Annandale believed that a slight change would enable other species to become established in the river above the delta. He cites a crab, *Varuna litterata* (Fabricius), as one species which migrates overland in vast numbers during the rainy season each year, but does not become established because crabs of the family *Potamonidae* already occupy favorable situations and can not be dislodged. A hydroid, *Campanulina ceylonensis* (Browne), also spreads continually but is eliminated in water which is so fresh that its specific gravity falls below 1.006.

As a result of his studies of the Thames River, Robson (1925) states that there are usually three elements in an estuarine fauna: (1) permanent indigenous species, (2) seasonal migrants, and (3) stragglers. He found that a holothurian, a chaetognath, four mollusks, a few species of copepods, and a shrimp, *Palaemonetes varians* Leach, were restricted to brackish water. He agrees with Annandale that few marine species became established in fresh water by migrating through estuaries. Thorpe (1927) studied estuaries in Sussex, England, and reached similar conclusions.

Various species are doubtless kept from spreading from the ocean through estuaries into fresh water because salinity falls below their limits of toleration. In the estuaries of the Rivers Tamar and Lyner in Great Britain, Percival (1929) found that the number of marine species decreased greatly when salinity fell below 3%, but some persisted in salinity as low as 2.1%. Littoral species showed greater toleration for low salinities than others. In Holland, Redeke (1922) studied the distribution of brackish-water animals in relation to salinity and found that they were divisible into three groups as shown in Table I.

TABLE I

REDEKE'S (1922) GROUPS OF BRACKISH-WATER ANIMALS; HOLLAND

Oligohalinophil	Mesohalinophil	Polyhalinophil
Coccinodiscus rothi	*Coccinodiscus biconicus*	*Coccinodiscus grani*
Thalassiosira baltica batava	*Thalassiosira baltica*	*Thalassiosira excentrica*
	Chaetoceras subtile	
Chaetoceras mülleri	*Eurytemora hirudinoides*	*Chaetoceras debile*
Eurytemora affinis	*Acartia bifolosa*	*Eurytemora hirudo*
Gammarus pulex	*Gammarus locusta*	*Acartia discaudata*
	Corophium lacustre	*Gammarus locusta*
	Corophium grossipes	*Corophium lacustre*

At the mouth of the Elbe River, Schliënz (1923) studied the distribution of 21 species of crustaceans between Hamburg and Cruxhaven, where salinities ranged from 0.47 to 17.12. His list included 1 crab, 1 shrimp, 3 schizopods, 10 amphipods, and 6 isopods. All these except one isopod (Asellus, which was only found in fresh water), occurred at the mouth of the river and gradually disappeared upstream. Only one species, *Gammarus locusta campylops* G. O. Sars, ranged throughout the region. Schliënz numbered his stations from the mouth upstream, 1 to 26. The ranges of the species were as follows:

Species	*Stations*	*Lowest Salinity*
Crago vulgaris (Fabricius)	1-13	0.43
Carcinas maenas Fabricius	1-8	6.82
Neomysis vulgaris Thompson	1-23	0.37
Praunus flexuosus Müller	1-5	13.50
Macropsis slabberi (V. Beneden)	1-4	13.97
Corophium curvispinum devium G. O. Sars, Wundsch.	20-26	0.0-0.5
Gammarus locusta campylops G. O. Sars	1-26	0.37
Corophium lacustre Vanh.	8-14	0.37
Gammarus duebenii Liljeborg	1-10	4.40

Corophium volvulator (Pallas)	1-9	5.90
Leptocheurus hirsutimanus Zadd.	9	5.90
Orchestia gamarellus (Pallas)	1-4, 9	5.90
Gammarus locusta (L.)	1-6	13.15
Gammarus marinus Leach	1-5	13.50
Taliturus saltator (Mont.)	1, 5	13.50
Asellus aquaticus (L.)	17, 21-26	0-0.5
Sphaeroma rugicauda Leach	5-9	5.90
Idothea viridis G. O. Sars	1-6	13.15
Jaera marina (Fabricius)	1-4	13.97
Idothea baltica (Pallas)	1-3	15.36
Ligyda oceania (L.)	1-3	15.36

Clearly these crustaceans also fall into three groups in their relations to salinity.

Goodhart (1941) divides the amphipods in an estuary on the coast of Hampshire into four groups that include: (1) two fresh-water species that can endure no salt, (2) six brackish-water species that cannot live permanently in either salt water or fresh water, (3) eight marine species that can endure some dilution of sea water, and (4) many marine species that do not occur in fresh water. Gunter (1942) gives a list of 141 species of fishes that live in salt water or fresh water. He points out (1947) that many primitive fishes are euryhaline. He also states that marine fishes are found nine times as often in fresh water as *vice versa.* So, most estuarine animals are marine. Marine animals tend to grow smaller in fresh water.

Prenant (1929) has called attention to the fact that the distribution of marine species in estuaries is correlated with respiratory requirements. As water becomes less saline, respiration becomes more difficult. The circulation of water by currents may in part compensate for the difficulties associated with lowered salinity. Of course variations in salinity have other effects on organisms besides those connected with respiration. These will be considered more fully in Chapter III, under Salinity.

There are a few animals which can survive direct transfer from ocean to fresh water, and there are many marine animals which live at times in fresh water or in diluted sea water (Pearse, 1929; Schlieper, 1929a; Sumner, 1906; Vaughan, 1919). As would be expected, small marine animals usually have less ability to live in diluted sea water than large animals. Young animals are generally less resistant but often possess "greater capacity to acclimate" (Andrews, 1925). Invertebrates with hard exoskeletons or slimy coverings are more resistant to changes in salinity than those without such protection. Brues (1927) kept a portunid crab, *Callinectes ornatus* Ordway, alive in fresh water for three months. Along the coast of Holland shrimps (*Crago vulgaris* Fabricius) migrate from salt to brackish water in spring, and immature individuals move further inland than adults (Havinga, 1930). According to Harms (1929), 22 species of selachians are established in fresh water, and tides have been an important factor in facilitating their passage through estuaries. The clams belonging to the family *Dreisensidae* have apparently spread from the Black Sea and established typical species after entering rivers (Andrusov, 1897). The Black Sea was probably more salty and characteristically marine in the past than it is now.

In estuaries not all types of spreading animals are moving upstream. Some fresh-water species are making progress toward the ocean. For example, various lines of evidence indicate that insects had their origin on land. Many of them have since invaded fresh water and a few have become established in or on the sea. Several species of water striders skim over the surface of the open ocean. The more specialized insects appear to be able to endure high salinity better than more primitive types (Buxton, 1926; Thorpe, 1927). Chironomid larvae endure variations in salinity better than corixids. Among the insects as a whole, the flies (Diptera) have been the most successful colonizers of the sea. Some of them live in water which is much saltier than the ocean (Beattie, 1932; Pearse, 1931, 1932e; Vogel, 1927). Bony fishes appear to have originated in fresh water and to have spread to all parts of the ocean.

An estuary has been called "the doorway by which marine forms have populated fresh water." This statement is perhaps in part true, but an estuarine doorway is not wide open and easily passed. There are many difficulties to be surmounted. Many animals struggle long ages to get through and fail. Only a few attain fresh water by this route.

Pools, Swamps, and Marshes

Marshes and swamps resemble estuaries and are often connected with them. They are always shallow; the amount of water in them varies more or less at different seasons; they contain considerable submerged and emergent vegetation, such as eel grasses, potamogetons, rushes, and grasses. A salty or brackish marsh near the sea may be subject to tidal influences; a fresh-water inland swamp may be overflowed during heavy rains or become nearly dry at other times. Pools are like marshes and swamps in many respects, but are largely without emergent aquatic vegetation.

Stagnant, shallow, vegetation-filled bodies of water near the ocean often tend to become fresher. In a Long Island, N. Y., salt marsh, Conrad & Galligar (1929) found that fresh-water vegetation advanced seaward and that salt-water plants retreated before them. Such migrations were in part due to the filling in of the land. On the coast of Tunis in areas which are periodically submerged by the ocean, dried, and subjected to rainfall, only ephemeral halophytes grow; but in similar areas which are not submerged, marshes develop in which Salicornia is the dominant plant (Burollet, 1926). Salt in itself is apparently not the chief factor in making the difference between an ocean beach and a marsh, but several factors are concerned. Animals which live in marshes, swamps, and pools are often subjected to extreme variations in temperature, salinity, essential gases in the water, and in available water. In a South American tropical swamp Carter & Beadle (1930) found that fishes survived temperatures as high as 42°C. during the middle of the day. The plankton animals died when temperatures reached 42° to 43°C. and were thus often living near their limits of toleration.

Fig. 5. A salt marsh in Colon, Panama. (Photo by R. H. Arnett, Jr.)

As a small body of water evaporates, its salinity may become very high. In Italy, Brighenti (1929) studied the animals in the Mesola salt marshes, which reached salinities as high as 41 grams per liter in summer but were nearly fresh in winter. He found a varied fauna which included ciliates (*Tintinnidae*) and foraminiferans (Trochomorpha). In deeper water were many amphipods, isopods, clams, snails, bryozoans, anemones, and annelids. A few animals ranged from fresh water to the sea—shrimps, anemones, clams, ciliates, etc.; others were found only in the salt marshes. On the coast of California ciliates have been collected in marshes where salinities were 7.5, 12.3, and 20 (Kirby, 1932). After studying the salt marshes of Croisic, Labbé (1926) concluded that most of the animals present had come from the ocean, and that some were making progress toward fresh water. In Norfolk, England, a littoral anemone (*Sagartia luciae* Verrill) was found living in water which had a salinity of 14.56 parts per thousand. In Algeria, Beadle (1943) studied 60 limited bodies of water that were more or less saline. He says, "The few marine types (e.g., the diatom *Chaetoceras* sp. and the alga *Enteromorpha intestinalis*) are found only in relatively low salinities. The majority are of fresh-water origin, including those adapted to the most saline waters." He found layering to be common in pools. A hot saline layer might be overlaid by a cooler, fresher layer. The lower layer might contain high H_2S and high O_2 simultaneously.

Probably because swamps and marshes are often deficient in oxygen, many animals which live in them are air breathers. Especially at night in the tropics the oxygen in shallow water often disappears altogether. This happens because high temperature makes the solubility of gases in water less and because the activities of bacteria and other organisms use oxygen rapidly. In Siam and India there are about twenty-five species of fishes which breathe air and drown if kept under water for from half an hour to two hours (Das, 1927). The snails in swamps in both tropical and temperate regions are commonly pulmonates; whereas those that live in streams, where there is plenty of oxygen, are generally branchiate. Probably lack of oxygen more than the periodic drying up of swamps has made paludine animals air breathers (Carter & Beadle, 1930; Pearse, 1932).

Gulick (1948) asserts that all terrestrial gastropods probably came from pond snails. They must remain moist, and they seal themselves into their shells when dried. Their slime prevents desiccation and they conserve water by excreting uric acid. Bassindale (1942) studied the toleration of amphipods on the coast of Great Britain for various salinities. *Gammarus pulex* was intolerant of salt and tidal rhythms; *G. duebeni* (+20-25), *G. zaddaci* (+28), and *G. locusta* (+28) had some toleration for various salinities, and *Marinogammarus marinus* was markedly stenohaline and found only in the sea.

Most people think of mosquito larvae as characteristic of stagnant pools. Arnett (1950) has given an excellent account of the habitat preferences of those in Panama. He makes the following groups of situations with the number of species indicated that have been found in each:

- Surface water
  - Flowing
    - Shady 5
    - Sunny 9
  - Stagnant (Permanent)
    - Shady 13
    - Sunny 25
  - Stagnant (Temporary) 7
  - Crab holes 2
- Aerial habitats
  - Close to the ground (Buttress roots, bamboo sections, coconut shells, palm spathes, etc.) 10
  - Leaf and flower bracts of terrestrial plants 6
  - Tree holes 9
  - Epiphytic bromeliads 5
- Artificial containers 10

Arnett also states that classifications might be made on the basis of toleration to salinity or whether water is foul, clear, turbid, etc.

Some larvae are associated with particular species of plants. Some are strictly vegetarian, but nine species are listed that are predators on other mosquito larvae.

When marshes, swamps, and pools periodically dry up, many of the animals which live in such situations are able to survive. Paludine types are commonly able to burrow, encyst, or go into some other type of dormancy. The ability of the lung-fishes to live in a cocoon of mud for months is well known (Smith, 1931). Hall (1901) describes the habits of two eel-like galaxid fishes from Tasmania and New Zealand. These burrow in mud or soil. One swims freely in water, but the other is accustomed to live in mud, swims with difficulty, and dies quickly when submerged in clear water. In Siam aestivating fishes burrow as much as two feet in soil and remain without water for three or four months. When the rainy season comes, serpent heads and climbing perch commonly migrate over the land (Smith, 1927). In Australia there are dragon-fly nymphs which can live in sand without water. Their bodies become so dry that they crackle when handled, but when such animals are put in water they become active in a few minutes (Tillyard, 1917). In Hawaii some dragon-fly nymphs have left the water altogether. They lurk at the bases of leaves and watch for prey (Perkins, 1897). The phyllopods and certain other small animals that live in temporary pools on prairies and steppes are able to stand great variations in environmental conditions. The eggs of some pool crustaceans will not hatch until they have been dried and subjected to extreme temperatures (Davenport, 1908).

The peculiar combination of variable environmental factors which obtains in marshes, swamps, and pools is conducive to the production of hardy animals and modifications toward land types. Variable temperatures and salinities permit only animals to survive which are able to stand such changes. Lack of oxygen and water makes air breathing and coverings which resist desiccation essential. With these qualities it is not difficult for animals to change from marshy ocean to swampy fresh water or from aquatic habitats to land. Paludal environments apparently have been important highways from sea to land.

Case (1919) believes that tetrapod vertebrates came into existence when paludal conditions obtained over wide areas of the earth. Many paleontologists agree that bony fishes had their origin in fresh water and that land vertebrates came largely from swamps.

Fig. 6. Animals on a marine mud flat There is little or no oxygen in the mud, so animals breathe by creating respiratory currents. (From Miner, 1912.) Courtesy of the American Museum of Natural History.

"Indeed, it may now be said to be highly probable that although no known genus of lobed-finned fish was the immediate ancestor of the amphibians, yet the group as a whole has the characters to be expected in the descendants of an earlier common stock that gave rise, on the left to the lung-fishes, near the center to the known lobe-fins, and on the right to the earliest tetrapods or amphibians" (Gregory, 1933).

Subterranean Habitats

Subterranean animals live where environmental conditions are quite stable. They are in little danger of injury by desiccation; they are not subject to sudden and extreme changes in temperature; and they are by their mode of life concealed from many predaceous enemies. At times soil animals suffer from lack of oxygen, especially during rainy weather when the water content of the soil is high; sometimes soil reactions change beyond their limits of toleration; but in general they enjoy a considerable degree of stability and safety. They of course have to pay the penalty that nature exacts from all specialists. Their distance-perceptive organs, sight and hearing, are often feeble, and they depend largely on contact senses, such as touch, taste, and smell, in their responses to environment. The soil has been invaded by arthropods and vertebrates which come from ancestral stocks which long ago enjoyed an epigean existence. On the other hand, some soil animals such as earthworms, apterygotid insects, tipulid and tabanid fly larvae perhaps spread from aquatic habitats and thus became dwellers in soil instead of in muddy, sandy, or rocky bottoms.

But even along the seashore burrowers are specialists. Certain sponges, worms, echinoderms, mollusks, and crustaceans are able to bore into rock (Russell & Yonge, 1928), and thus find safe retreats on wave-swept shores. Marine burrowers generally attain environmental stability. Reid (1930) found that the water from a fresh-water stream which flows over a sandy beach on the seashore produced no effect on the salinity in the sand below 25 cm. Some worms at low tide burrowed deeper, thus avoided the diluted water, and were able to establish themselves in the estuary of a stream. But fossorial habits always tend to make animals specialists. Marine worms, crustaceans, and clams often have elaborate adaptations for protecting their respiratory cavities (Garstang, 1905) and for breathing in water. Many make characteristic protective tubes of various types.

A few crabs and other crustaceans (Uca, Macrophthalmus, Gecarcinus, Ocypode, Thalassina, Birgus, etc.; Pearse, 1914a, 1929, 1929a, 1931; Verwey, 1927) have quite evidently spread from burrows along the seashore to burrows farther inland, but none of these have become dominant land animals which play an important rôle in terrestrial life as a whole.

The earthworms are probably about the only group of dominant land animals that may have spread from aquatic habitats through the soil. Such careful studies of soil animals as Cameron (1913), Bornebusch (1930), and others have made show that, except for earthworms, dominant soil animals belong largely to modern groups such as Diptera, Coleoptera, and certain Myriapoda. Primitive apterous insects are present in great numbers near the surface and extend down to depths of as much as two meters (Shelford, 1929), but they constitute a very small part of the mass of animals that occurs in soils. It is possible, however, that such minute insects have spread from ancient seashores, as some live in such situations today, and thus have gradually invaded the soils far from water.

A few animals have become established as specialized permanent residents of caves. Certain of the more specialized of these lack pigment, and have degenerate visual organs and enlarged tactual organs. Some of them also occur in underground waters and at times are taken from wells or appear in epigean habitats. Some cave fishes and crustaceans may be said to have rather definite affinities with marine animals (Eigenmann, 1898, 1909; Pearse *et al.*, 1935) and doubtless are relics of a fauna which inhabited the caves when they were submarine or littoral (Davis, 1931). However, the fauna of caves as a whole consists of representatives of rather recent and specialized groups (bats, salamanders, beetles, flies, spiders, and crayfishes), as well as archaic, primitive types. "Temporary residents and some of the less highly specialized cave inhabitants are widely distributed and usually apparently cave forms of long standing. . . . The nearest relatives of cave animals are nocturnal, or are dark or shade-loving species. Accidents play no part, or at most a very small part, in the origin of cave inhabitants. Animals have reached caves by active migration into places where they find conditions suitable for their existence. Cave species are

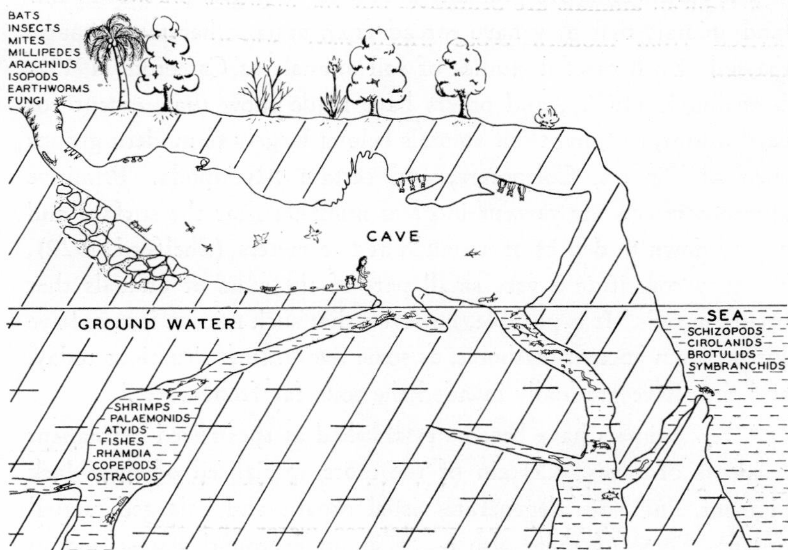

Fig. 7. A cross-section of a cave in Yucatan showing the affinities of the cave animals.

fitted for cave life before entering caves. Cave species may arise from highly modified animals living outside of caves going directly into the deeper parts of caves, or they may arise gradually by the collecting about the mouths of caves of forms slightly modified" (Banta, 1907). Concerning a recent survey of 41 caves in West

Virginia, Reese (1932) says: Cave crickets and certain Diptera were found in practically all caves; bats in the majority of the caves; fish and salamanders in a few caves. No blind fish were found. Blind beetles were the only blind animals seen." In this case the animals mentioned as being abundant are all recent specialized types.

The soil and the caves included below it contain few animals that have spread from the ocean or fresh water into them. A few such subterranean animals are primitive, but the majority are apparently derived from modern types which have spread from epigean habitats.

Dilution and Salation

Of the earth's surface 73.4% is ocean and 26.6% is land. The salinities of various enclosed parts of seas are somewhat different. The Caribbean and Gulf of California are "normal" with salinities of 35-36 and 35-35.5; the Red Sea (37-41), Persian Gulf (37-38), and Mediterranean Sea (37-39) are above normal; and the Arctic (20-35), Japan (30-34), China (25-35), and Baltic (3-15) Seas are below normal (Jenkins, 1935).

Many littoral marine animals are able to live in diluted sea water (Vaughan, 1919; Fredericq, 1922). Such types as the worms of the genera Nereis and Laonice and the king crab, Limulus, will live for weeks in a mixture of one quarter sea water and three quarters fresh water (Pearse, 1928). Some animals (echinoderms) in which the body fluids are nearly isotonic with the surrounding medium are killed when obliged to live in diluted sea water, but others (certain crabs and fishes) can survive gradual or even sudden changes. The hagfish, a primitive cyclostome, has body fluids which are isotonic with the surrounding medium. "The chloride content of the blood of the hag-fish, *Polistotrema stouti* (Lockington), is comparable to that of the marine invertebrates, and it is probable that part of the body wall of this species is freely permeable to water and salts.

This is interpreted as indicating that the hag-fish had no fresh water ancestors" (Bond, Cary, & Hutchinson, 1932).

The waters in the great seas of the earth constitute a great physical-chemical system which maintains more or less stability. Changes in the open sea, except for temporary surface dilutions resulting from rains, are chiefly due to the activities of organisms (McClendon, 1918). In warm seas water is supersaturated with calcium carbonate, and lime is continually precipitated out, largely through the activities of organisms. Bottom deposits in parts of the ocean within the 2000 meter contour may contain 1/2 to 2/3 lime (Johnstone, 1908). Ocean water contains a great variety of substances in solution in forms available for use by plants and animals. Marine animals make use of such metals as copper, zinc, iron, and manganese (Phillips, 1922). With the inflowing waters from land areas also come various substances. Among these, compounds which contain nitrogen in available forms are of primary importance. They result to a considerable extent from the work of nitrogenous bacteria, which are largely confined to the land. Because fresh water has average depths that are much less than those in oceans, light should be available more generally for photosynthesis and the initiation of the manufacture of basic foods. But fresh water, because it is shallow, is usually more turbid than sea water, and thus the penetration of light is prevented. It also remains more turbid because precipitation is more rapid in salt water. When the fundamental needs of the basic activities of protoplasm are considered, there are desiderata in both fresh water and sea water. In the past and at present animals are struggling to pass from one to the other. Usually the chief limiting factor in the productiveness of any area is available food. Nitrogen and phosphorous compounds are perhaps those which most often are present in minimum amounts and thus limit the manufacture of organic foods, growth, and reproduction.

There are many examples of animals that have been cut off from the ocean and persisted in bodies of water that gradually became fresher, so that they finally became fresh water animals. In the deep lakes in the northern United States (Hoy, 1873), Canada (Adamstone, 1924), and Scandinavia (Ekman, 1920, 1930) there are shrimps (Mysis), amphipods (Pontoporeia), and other animals which belong to genera and families which still exist in the ocean and are looked upon as representative marine animals. Ponds and pools in sandy beaches which have been cut off from the sea remain fresher than the neighboring marine areas, even though they are subject to tidal influences by percolation of water through the sand. Such ponds are inhabited by marine burrowing animals (Calianassa), and such marine fishes as mullets and needle-fishes may persist, but, as the ponds grow fresher, they are soon invaded by progressive and aggressive types of insects, such as various Diptera, Coleoptera, Hemiptera, and Odonata (Pearse, 1932). On the beaches in Puget Sound, Miles (1920) observed three species of blennies that lived near low tide mark. He believed they chose this habitat because oxygen was more abundant there. Mytilus eggs, sperms, and larvae do not survive in salinities that are slightly below those of sea water, and these clams are absent from quiet waters (Young, 1941). A beach snail in Florida (*Thais floridana*) became immobile and died in low salinities (Schechter, 1943).

It has been claimed that some lakes, like Tanganyika, have a "marine" fauna (Moore, 1903; Germain, 1913), but "recent discoveries do not favor Moore's hypothesis of a marine Jurassic origin for Tanganyika . . . there is no support for the view that the ocean at one time extended over the Congo basin. . . . The view that Tanganyika owes its remarkable organisms to a prolonged period of isolation is regarded as the most likely suggestion" (Cunnington, 1920).

The mollusks in the lake, however, show both marine and freshwater affinities. Schweitz & Darteville (1948) believe this may have been brought about by the lake drying out and becoming more saline; then with more rains again developing fresh-water forms that come in from rivers and ponds. Certain blind cave fishes have affinities with marine groups and have apparently remained in cave waters as they freshened (Eigenman, 1909; Pearse, 1938). On the northern border of the Sahara, Gauthier (1927) found a species of shrimp in an isolated spring-fed desert reservoir. He believed this crustacean had been marooned when the course of a river changed.

In many small bodies of water which are cut off from the ocean, salinity increases much above that of sea water. In isolated inland pools also evaporation may cause salinity to become very high. In such situations the salts present may differ in character and relative amount from those in the sea. When water evaporates from a salt-containing basin, salts will precipitate out in a certain order; double salts may be formed and separate again when rains dilute the water (Richardson, 1928). In so-called magnesium sulphate lakes in the Caucasus, Wornichin (1926) describes three characteristic stages: (1) a period when there is little salt and Ruppia is the dominant plant; (2) a freshening of the water and an increase in Vaucheria and other plants; and (3) an increase in salinity and the formation of felt-like growths of plants. In Devil's Lake, North Dakota, live several species of fresh-water rotifers which have become adapted to life in brackish water (about 1% salt) which is unlike the sea in salt content (Bryce, 1925). Perhaps fresh-water animals are less likely to become adjusted to salt water than are salt-water animals to become adjusted to various dilutions. For example, in the Kaiser Wilhelm Canal, which runs from the North Sea to the East Sea and connects with the River Eider, Brandt (1896) found that animals had entered from either end and become established in waters which varied in salt content from 4.7 to 19.0 parts *pro mille,* but only a few stonefly and beetle larvae had come in from fresh water. However, paleontological evidence indicates that in the past the sea has been invaded from fresh water or from land by bony fishes, pinnipeds, several orders of reptiles, and other animals.

Under experimental conditions fishes have been gradually adjusted to water of higher salinity than the ocean. Richet (1926) kept a fish, *Diplodus sargus* (Gmelin), for 7.5 months as the salt content of the medium was raised to 52.1 grams per liter. The fish died when the salinity was decreased to 31.0. In Japan a student working in Professor N. Yatsu's laboratory in 1930 showed the writer specimens of the fish, *Oryzias latipes* (Temminck & Schlegel), which were living in small aquaria in which salinities had been gradually increased. Some had reached salinities as high as 60.0. Rees (1941) in rock pools on the shores of Wales observed *Monocelis fusca.* When transferred from normal sea water to higher salinities the worm endured those as high as 76.8, but when water was allowed to evaporate gradually it lived in 109-120. Certain insects are able to live in high salinities. Ephydrid fly larvae live in the Great Salt Lake, Utah. In Japan the mosquito larvae live in littoral rock pools in salinities as high as 42.0 (Pearse, 1931). At Dry Tortugas mosquito and dragon-fly larvae live in salinities as high as 72.0 and 62.0, respectively (Pearse, 1932e). Animals which live in solutions which contain salts or in solutions which have osmotic pressures which are above or below those of their own body fluids do not vary internally as the surrounding medium varies so that they become isotonic with it. They are animals that have attained some degree of internal stability and thus become more or less independent of the environment (Pike & Scott, 1915; Pearse, 1931, 1932b). There have been many ad- and ab-oceanic migrations in the past and such are taking place today. Animals along beaches in general are able to endure greater variations in environment than those in estuaries and hence more often become established in media which differ from those in which their ancestors lived.

Islands

Islands surrounded by ocean are more or less isolated environmental units which usually have a fauna and flora limited to comparatively few species (Stefani, 1929; Gulick, 1932). Such an area as an island offers is soon invaded by animals which have recently come from the ocean, especially crustaceans such as the crabs belonging to the genera Ocypode and Geograpsus; terrestrial hermit crabs (Coenobita, Birgus); isopods; and amphipods. The food of such animals is chiefly vegetation and organic refuse (Andrews, 1900; Borradaile, 1903; Pearse, 1929, 1931). Gulick (1932) has emphasized the fact that isolated islands are not populated by land plants, snails, and vertebrates by spreading migrations from the ocean, though he admits that such animals as the gobies that live in Hawaiian streams have come from the neighboring littoral waters. "Really radical new departures seem to require a longer time allowance than these geologically not very permanent islands can furnish." Gulick believes that insular animals such as he discusses are disseminated by wind storms and flight, and to a less extent by transportation on flotsam. The seeds of some island plants remain viable after being immersed in sea water for from thirty to ninety days (Borza & Bujorean, 1927).

The islands Verlaten and Krakatoa, which lie between Java and Sumatra, were covered by volcanic ashes in 1883, and most or all of the life on them was thus destroyed. Dammerman (1926, 1928) has studied the repopulation of these islands. He observed that the first animals to appear were largely vegetarians and scavengers. A large percentage of these were animals that were able to fly or balloon. Within a few years land crustaceans, land mollusks, earthworms, lizards, and snakes were present. It is possible that life was not completely destroyed on these islands (Scharff, 1926; Backer, 1930), but Dammerman states that the islands were covered with hot ashes to depths of thirty to sixty meters and that no plants or animals could have survived.

Oceanic islands have apparently not played an important rôle in the evolution of land animals from the ocean, but have often furnished habitats which were taken advantage of by animals which could in some way reach them.

LAND ELEVATION

Land elevation and the resulting better aeration of ground water may permit littoral animals to migrate inland through the soil (Harms, 1932). To the writer's knowledge no accurate observations have been made as to what the actual effects of such elevations are. During the great earthquake in Japan in 1923 the shore line at the Biological Station at Misaki rose four feet. Dr. N. Yatsu, the director of the station, states that most of the marine animals which were elevated above their optimum zone soon died and that there was a great decrease in the numbers of littoral animals for several years. A very gradual elevation of a beach might be conducive to the assumption of land life by certain littoral animals. The answer to the question waits for evidence.

3

CAUSES OF EMIGRATIONS FROM THE SEA

THOUGH there is little doubt that most groups of animals had their origin in the ocean and gradually invaded fresh-water and land habitats, there is perhaps some uncertainty as to why animals should leave the stable, dependable ocean and migrate into highly variable situations where life is perhaps more exciting but at the same time more precarious. Some who have considered this question believe that "lures" of various sorts have enticed animals from their ancestral homes (Hesse, 1920), and there appears to be evidence to support such a view. But it is also evident that some animals have been forced to leave the ocean to escape from dangers which threatened racial extinction. Perhaps some also left because of factors which were neither attractive nor repellant. Heape (1931) lists three incentives to emigration: (1) food, (2) climate, and (3) overpopulation.

SPREADING

Probably all species of animals and plants tend to extend their ranges by spreading into all available habitats. Multiplication of individuals leads to overpopulation. In nature various factors operate as checks which keep the numbers of individuals at certain

Fig. 8. A coral reef on the north coast of Barbados. The reef and rock cliffs shelter many animals that live alternately in the water and the air as the tide changes. (Photo by R. E. Blackwelder.)

levels. If environment or species change and disturb the existing balance, then numbers may increase or decrease. No matter how specialized an animal may become in its relation to environment, it can never lose its ability to spread. Johnstone (1908) says, "Yet the limitation of habitat is partially compensated for by the evolution of larval stages in the life history of an organism. We nearly always find that a sessile benthic animal has evolved a free-swimming larval stage; or the primitive pelagic form has evolved a sessile habitat during the latter period of its life history." Even parasites which are securely nestled within favorable hosts at intervals spread into the outside world. Some of them have very special and elaborate means for doing so. Certain parasites are always spread by bloodsuckers such as mosquitoes, ticks, or leeches.

To maintain even a small place in the world, a species must have a chance to spread. If this continual pressure to invade new situations is inherent in all organisms, it may at times, when circumstances are especially favorable, move certain animals out of the ocean into littoral, estuarine, or paludal habitats. Most of the available niches are already filled, but when a new area is available it is quickly populated. In this connection Hubbs cites "the bizarre evolution of cichlids in the great lakes of Africa; the multiplication of cyprinids from a single species in Lake Lanao, Mindanao (Herre); and the very rich fauna of the Rio Lerma system in Mexico, largely made up of 2 species groups." Price & Gunter (1943) describe the effects of climatic changes in Texas. In 1870 some streams dried up and have been intermittent since. Then live oaks died and there were other changes in vegetation. Tall grass was replaced by brush jungles and animals of arid regions, such as the armadillo and coati mundi, spread north and east.

Succession

Organisms invade habitats in an orderly manner. If a new area is opened for colonization, it is generally occupied at first by a few pioneers. These with the progressive physical and chemical changes which occur in all habitats prepare the way for other plants and animals. Then during a transition stage the number of species increases, and an area often becomes thickly populated. Finally certain species which, because they happen to fit the conditions at the particular time and place, become the dominant types and thus constitute what ecologists call a climax formation. When a bit of land sinks below the ocean it is populated in a more or less orderly way by marine plants and animals. The same is true when a portion of sea bottom is elevated into the air, when a landslide denudes a part of a mountain side, or when any environmental change opens a new area into which plants and animals may spread.

Succession and spreading together continually give animals opportunities to explore and occupy new situations. A slight fluctuation in environment may change the course of succession and lead to a different climax formation. A particular species, if accidentally introduced into an area early, becomes dominant; whereas if it arrives later in the successional series and has to compete with organisms that are already established, it may never be able to do so (Scott, 1910). Succession results in part from the effects of environmental changes, particularly those brought about by the presence of certain organisms which prepare the way for others, and in part from competition between species. Competition and differences in the physical-chemical qualities in environments bring about the segregation of animals into specific habitats.

McDougall (1943), Pyefinch (1943), and Weiss (1948) have studied the repopulation of bare rocks and other hard surfaces in the ocean. At first, such types as barnacles and oysters predominate, but these usually are later smothered by hydroids, sponges, tunicates, and bryozoans. All these sessile animals vary with the seasons. They have no chance of attaining terrestrial life.

Segregation

Animals tend to segregate into groups which become subspecies and in time species. It is generally believed that the ranges of closely related subspecies and species are usually different (Jordan, 1905; Sumner, Osburn, and Cole, 1913; Sumner, 1932), but it is not always so (Richards & Robson, 1926; Pearse, 1933, 1934). This means that competing species usually are not closely related (Robertson, 1906). A group of animals which can find an unoccupied environmental niche escapes certain competitions that its ancestors were obliged to endure. Though subspecies may intergrade along the borders of their ranges, they may be so stable that they will breed true for generations when isolated (Sumner, 1929). New races often originate at localities which are remote from those occupied by the parent stock (Sumner, 1928). Two kinds of changes may be said to take place in animals: (1) geographical, which are often adaptive, and (2) constitutional, which also may be adaptive or not (Crampton, 1925).

In their relations with each other, animals may be individualistic or socialistic, as individuals or as species. They may compete and struggle against each other for things in the environment, or they may coöperate in such a way as to help each other to survive in the struggle for existence. When two species contest for a habitat one may be better adapted to survive in it than the other and finally dominate. A maladapted species may survive for a long time in a habitat if it is without competition, but, when it competes with species which are better fitted to survive under the given conditions, it soon becomes extinct (Warming, 1909). An animal to survive must continually struggle to overcome environmental resistance, and if its biotic potential is not sufficient to compensate for biological as well as physical-chemical environmental factors which are unfavorable, it cannot survive (Chapman, 1931).

Many animals are especially adapted to avoid competition. Robertson (1906) says, "Species are characterized by non-competitive habits rather than adaptive structures." Certain plethodontid salamanders segregate most sharply into habitats during their breeding periods. They avoid competition by selecting different humidities, different types of streams, etc. (Noble, 1927). Vestal (1914) has gone so far as to enumerate five types of characters which remove animals from competition: (1) structural, which give animals special advantages in particular habitats (as the legs of a mole); (2) physiological, such as ability to digest and assimilate unusual foods (clothes moth eats keratin) or to exist in peculiar environments (anaerobic animals); (3) psychological, such as preferences for special foods or habitats; (4) biological, which permit adaptation of life cycles to favorable seasons, feeding to particular times of day, etc.; and (5) numerical by which the numbers of a species are adjusted to food supply or other limiting environmental factors. When a new area is opened for population, competition may be suspended for a time (Borradaile, 1923). Overpopulation may lead to extreme competition, epidemics, and consequent decrease in numbers. Thus a small group of peculiar individuals may survive the period of stress and initiate a new race or species (Elton 1924).

Another way in which animals may segregate is through assortive mating (Poulton, 1908). Fulton (1933) recently separated three races of the cricket *Nemobuis fasciatus* (De Geer) chiefly because they have different songs. These races "are more distinct physiologically than morphologically," and "they seldom if ever interbreed under natural conditions." Probably there are other animals which have formed special groups and taken up life in particular habitats because of peculiar secondary sex characters. "The evolution of secondary sex characters is usually not progressive and continuous but hap-hazard and often parallel in not closely related stocks" (Noble, 1927). Perhaps it has permitted groups of animals to become adapted to new habitats.

Zonation and Stratification

On ocean beaches all over the earth animals are arranged more or less in zones (Allee, 1923, 1923a, 1923b; Crane, 1947; Evans, 1947; Hewatt, 1937; Kühnholtz-Lordat, 1926, 1926a; Pearse, 1914; Pearse, Humm, & Wharton, 1942; McDougall, 1943; Stephenson, 1942). Such tendencies toward stratification in the distribution of animals in habitats is general, and at times such segregation has apparent relation to differences in temperature, available water, and other environmental conditions. Even among land vegetation there is a tendency for plants and animals to segregate into strata, which begin below the surface of the soil and extend to the tree tops.

Along ocean beaches the tendency of animals to segregate into zones has apparently led to the taking up of life on land by some species. Along the Irish coast the distribution of salt-marsh plants is correlated with the salinity of the water in which they grow (McCrea, 1926). Where mangroves flourish on the coast of Java the littoral crustaceans are arranged in five rather definite zones through the tidal areas (Verwey, 1930). On the Scottish coast each species of intertidal animal reaches its maximum size at a certain level (Stephen, 1930, 1930a). On the French coast Fischer (1928) has attempted to discover the factors which determine the upper limits of distribution of intertidal marine animals. He finds that exposure of beaches to the open sea may cause waves to distort the zonation which is elsewhere dependent largely on tides. The alga *Fucus platycarpus* Farlow and the barnacle *Balanus balanoides* (L.) have upper limits at mean neap-tide level. "Various other littoral organisms have limits more or less close to high-tide mark or to low-tide mark; almost none stop in the intermediate zone. It is thus frequency rather than duration of immersion that acts upon organisms. Ecological subdivisions may be established in the tidal zone, corresponding to the successive upper limits of distribution of various species."

Prenant & Tessier (1924) have made a very careful study of the zonation of the sessile animals on the beaches at Roscoff, France, and cite the following factors which appear to be most important in limiting distribution: (1) Water level; a few species stand desiccation, but most are continually submerged. (2) Light; some species avoid light, apparently because their larvae are usually negatively phototropic. (3) Freshwater; hydroids and bryozoans have little resistance to dilution; some barnacles have much. (4) Sediment; some species depend on this and organic food in the water. (5) Clearness; some species are limited to clear water. (6) Nature of substratum; a very important influence, as Allee (1923b) also found. (7) Depth influences, desiccation, wave action, sediment, light, and other factors as well as pressure. (8) Danger, which these authors think is most important of all; most species they find to be arranged according to this. On the coast of Canada, Huntsman (1918a) found that vertical distribution of several littoral animals was limited largely by enemies.

Animals along the shores of all sorts of aquatic environments continually tend to spread into terrestrial habitats but are usually prevented from doing so by various factors. For example, Lieber (1931) thinks that limnodrilids might gradually become land animals if it were not for occasional high waters and frosts which prevent them from doing so. The evidence that many animals have left the sea and attained land life through the intertidal zone has already been reviewed. In this section the view is stressed that segregation into habitats, particularly zonation and stratification along beaches, has been a factor in the development of terrestrial animals.

Food

All animals require organic food. This they secure directly or indirectly from plants which are able to use radiant energy to manufacture new molecules. A few plants are able to build organic compounds without light, but these are exceptional, and most of the foods consumed by animals result from photosynthesis. As light is absorbed rapidly when passing through water, it is apparent that more energy is available on land for food building by plants than in water. In the ocean and in deep lakes photosynthesis is limited to a rather narrow stratum near the surface. Many streams are so turbid that little light can penetrate them.

Of course a plant requires more than light for the building of organic compounds. Water and chemical compounds which furnish carbon, nitrogen, phosphorus, and other essential elements in available forms are also necessary. Sea water probably contains all chemical elements, but some are present in minute quantities or unavailable forms. In the ocean there is more organic food near land. In the open sea there is often a scarcity of available carbon, phosphorus, and nitrogen compounds, and such materials are continually added to the sea from the land (Johnstone, 1908). On the land there is plenty of light everywhere, but the distribution of available water and favorable temperatures is often variable or discontinuous, and some essential elements, such as calcium or iodine, may be lacking. Most marine animals usually live in their food or have it brought to them in the water that surrounds them. Land animals to a greater extent are obliged to seek for foods which remain in particular places (Clark, 1925).

In the past the development of land animals was asscociated with terrestrial plants, which preceded them and furnished basic foods. The spermatophytes are largely confined to land habitats. Only about thirty species of them live even along the margins of the ocean (Buxton, 1926). Their tissues, and especially their seeds and fruits, furnish water and highly nutritious organic foods in concentrated forms. They have been an important factor in making life for land animals possible (Berry, 1920).

Along the shores of oceans the chief sources of food for marine animals are plankton, including minute types such as diatoms and desmids; organic debris, which may form bottom deposits or travel about in the water itself; organisms brought in by rivers; and jetsam such as accumulates along the drift line. Plant food in the ocean is usually comparatively limited except in cold seas (Harms, 1929). Among invertebrates, littoral marine animals feed largely on plankton, algae, or mud, but those which have taken up life on land are generally vegetarians (Borradaile, 1903; Pearse, 1929, 1932a; Watson, 1928). Land vertebrates are often carnivorous (Pearse, 1932a). The intertidal zone often furnishes an abundance of food and is invaded by both terrestrial and marine animals. In such migrations the vegetarians and scavengers usually precede the carnivores.

A sand beach at first glance appears to be a barren waste, but it contains many animals that are adapted to burrow and feed on plankton, and myriads of bacteria are continually converting organic debris into soluble foods that are returned to the sea (Pearse, Humm, & Wharton, 1942). On mud beaches burrowing animals commonly feed on bacteria (MacGinitie, 1935; Zobell & Feltham, 1938). It requires 10,000 pounds of plants to produce 100 pounds of clams (MacGinitie, 1935). At Tortugas, where there is constant high temperature and abundant light, Riley (1938) estimates that the amount of plankton is less than 4% of that in temperate regions, and states that nitrate is the chief limiting factor in food production. Putter's (1907) claim that dissolved food substances are absorbed through external membranes by aquatic animals has been discredited (Krogh, 1931). Such materials appear to be absorbed through the membranes of the digestive system.

There appears to be adequate evidence that various animals have left the ocean in order to take advantage of food resources on land. Along beaches today scavenger crabs which have recently come from the ocean contest for the carcasses of animals along the drift line with terrestrial flies and beetles. The archer fish in Siam shoots insects down into the water where it devours them, certain of the gobies run out over the land where they catch ants and spiders (Pearse, 1933), and climbing perch at twilight or during rains leave ponds and streams to search for insects in grassy fields. Various crabs have not left the ocean but continually run out over the land to hunt for food, and some of these (fiddler crabs) probably never seek food under water.

RESPIRATION

There are great differences in the amount of oxygen consumed by various marine animals. Baldwin (1924) gives the following figures, stated as cubic centimeters per gram per hour:

Animal	cc.	Animal	cc.
Mackerel	0.726	Nereis	0.291
Scup	0.301	Amphitrite	0.131
Sea bass	0.070	Cerebratula	0.172
Flounder	0.063	Starfish	0.019
Tautog	0.062	Sagartia	0.026
Squid	0.601	Dactylometra	0.019
Phascolosoma	0.367		

At 12° C. the oxygen consumption of the scup was reduced 21%; at 4° C., 40%. In light, a scup consumed 0.156 cc.; in dark, 0.115 cc. Evidently, more complex and active animals consume more oxygen than do simple sluggish animals.

Respiration is more difficult in fresh water than in the ocean, but currents may help compensate for lowered salinity (Prenant, 1929). The presence of monocarbonates in sea water makes the elimination of carbon dioxide easier. This factor alone prevents certain animals from invading brackish water. It is easier for marine animals to invade brackish water in the tropics than in cooler parts of the earth because monocarbonates are present (Schlieper, 1928). Marine fishes enter streams in the tropics more readily than elsewhere, probably because of the richer lime content there (Breeder, 1933).

Most animals require a more or less continuous supply of oxygen and give off carbon dioxide as a result of their metabolic activities. Carbon dioxide may accumulate and be present in such quantities as to be injurious to animals. This seldom occurs in the atmosphere but often does in small, shallow bodies of fresh water, especially if the bottom contains organic debris which by decaying uses up oxygen and produces carbon dioxide. Such animals as rotifers, nematodes, crustaceans, insects, and fishes may be poisoned by large amounts of carbon dioxide in water (Nikitinsky, 1928). On the other hand, many aerobic animals have remarkable ability to live in the absence of oxygen (Dakin, 1925). Fishes are very sensitive to small variations in the gases (O_2, CO_2, H_2S) dissolved in water (Shelford & Powers, 1915). The ability of fishes to extract oxygen from water depends upon the carbon dioxide tension in the water, the alkali reserve in their blood, and other factors (Powers, 1923, 1932).

Respiration is in some respects more difficult in water than air. The atmosphere always contains about 22% oxygen, and poisonous gases are rare. The amount of oxygen in the ocean is quite constant at all depths, but in small bodies of water it may vary from none to several cubic centimeters per liter. Furthermore, as water grows warmer, its power to hold gases in solution becomes progressively less. In the tropics, therefore, shallow bodies of water often lack sufficient oxygen for the respiratory needs of animals. Bog ponds in temperate or cool regions of the earth usually contain very little animal life. This is not only on account of the acids and other substances present, some of which are toxic, but also because of the lack of oxygen in winter when contact with the atmosphere is cut off by a coating of ice (Rigg, Thompson, Lorah, & Williams, 1927; Jewell & Brown, 1929). In the shallow klongs in Siam (Pearse, 1932) and in the tanks in India (Pruthi, 1933) there is little oxygen at night, and many fishes, snails, and other aquatic animals come to the surface to breathe in air. At the mouth of the Amazon River, the lung-fish Lepidosiren and the air-breathing eel Symbranchus live in water that contains very little oxygen and do the same (Carter, 1931; Beadle, 1943). Many river snails are branchiate, but most of those that live in ponds and small streams are pulmonates. Lite & Whitney (1925) studied the development of certain rotifers and found that most eggs develop normally if aerated, but that few will hatch unless they are placed in a decomposing mass of organic material before being aerated, so that the egg shells are broken down somewhat. These animals are thus adapted to conditions which normally obtain in swamps and pools.

Case (1919, 1926) and Romer (1945) on paleontological evidence favor the view that aquatic animals were forced to become terrestrial by progressively increasing aridity. Another possibility is furnished by the observations of Hora (1933) and the writer (1932a, 1933) in India and Siam, where there is heavy rainfall. In the latter country there are twenty-odd species of fishes that have developed various types of lungs for air-breathing as outpocketings from their gill cavities. These live in the shallow klongs, where the writer showed that oxygen may be low or absent altogether at night. Some of these fishes never leave the water but will suffocate if prevented from coming to the surface. At least two of these fishes (Ophiocephalus, Anabas) wander freely over the land, especially at night. The "climbing perch" seeks insects and other foods on land. The "serpent heads" live for more than two months without water, buried in dry rice fields. Siamese fishermen fish for them with spades. Perhaps lack of oxygen in limited bodies of fresh water, as well as aridity, has been a factor in causing animals to take up a terrestrial existence.

A marine sipunculid worm, *Physcosoma lurco* Sel. & de Man, lives in burrows in the intertidal zone between the roots of mangroves, along the shores of the Sunda Islands. It is actively homoiosmotic and typically marine. Because of lack of oxygen in its environment this worm has been forced, according to Harms & Dragendorff (1933) who have investigated it thoroughly, to leave the ocean and live in moist situations or beaches where oxygen can be obtained from the atmosphere. It cannot live without sea water and therefore is confined to the intertidal zone.

Enough has been said to show that the conditions of life in water are such that respiration at times becomes difficult or impossible. Animals thus tend to go to the surface where aeration is best or come to depend on the air above the surface for respiratory needs. Some animals, having thus become airbreathers, may wander out of aquatic habitats and finally become terrestrial animals. The respiratory difficulties in water and the advantages in the atmosphere thus contribute to the trend of life toward land.

Reproduction

An animal may live in a habitat where it has an abundance of food, where many other environmental conditions of life are favorable, and where it has few or no enemies, but if proper conditions for reproduction are lacking, the species will become extinct. Many animals leave situations were conditions for feeding and resting are highly desirable and make long migrations to localities where conditions for rearing young are more favorable. Many birds and mammals make annual journeys to particular breeding grounds and spend the remainder of the year where conditions are more desirable for the adults of their species.

An eel spends five to twenty years in fresh water, where it feeds and grows. Then it dons its silvery spawning dress and hastens back to the depths of the ocean to lay its eggs. The young eels spend one to three years in floating back to fresh-water streams and ponds. Salmon, on the other hand, hatch on the pebbly bottoms of cool, clear streams and lakes. After about a year in fresh water they make their way to the ocean, where they feed and grow. When mature salmon migrate up streams to seek out appropriate spawning beds, most species take no food and die after they have shed their gametes. "The stimulus to the performance of the spawning migration is the developing and ripening of the generative organs, and the elaboration of an internal secretion from the ovary or testis which produces an intoxication, and impels the fish to seek water of definite physical conditions. What these conditions may be depends on the former history of the species—the 'historical basis of acting' being the determining factor in this choice" (Johnstone, 1908). A species' area of reproduction may differ widely from that of its general distribution. An animal's requirements are often quite different at different periods in its life cycle.

In tropical America there is a swamp snail which always crawls out of water and lays its eggs, like piles of rosy pearls, in bunches on the stems of emergent plants. There are several species of frogs which in similar fashion deposit their eggs in frothy masses so that the young tadpoles when hatching will fall into the water below. The terrestrial marbled salamander long before rains leaves clutches of eggs on land under logs and around litter, choosing situations such that they may be submerged before they hatch (Noble & Brady, 1933). Some terrestrial salamanders have progressed further in their adaptation to terrestrial existence. They pass through all larval stages within egg membranes and are ready for life on land when they emerge.

In progressive adaptation from aquatic toward terrestrial life there is a general tendency to eliminate free-swimming stages in the life histories. Many marine gastropods hatch as swimming larvae; pond snails develop within the jelly deposited by their parents; land snails in logs or soil commonly deposit eggs which are surrounded by tough shells, and these hatch into little snails much like their parents. Decapod crustaceans commonly carry their eggs attached to the abdominal appendages. Gravid females of some littoral species run in and out of the water. Some fluviatile and terrestrial crabs do not return to the ocean to breed, but have become adjusted more or less to life in fresh water or on land. Many species of animals tend to segregate most sharply into particular habitats while breeding. Certain species of salamanders may often live together but when mating and spawning segregate into different situations (Noble, 1927).

Fig. 9. In a Colombian swamp a snail deposits its group of eggs above the surface of the water where there is an abundance of oxygen and more or less freedom from aquatic predators.

Animals continually seek suitable breeding sites. This leads such animals as wasps and birds to resort to craggy cliffs; certain birds and seals seek out barren ocean islands; and other birds fly far to the Arctic barren lands. To attain proper conditions animals also leave the ocean for fresh water and aquatic habitats on land. Thus they secure safety, aeration, and other desiderata. The seeking of peculiar breeding conditions has been a factor in the development of terrestrial animals.

Safety

Animals have often taken up temporary or permanent refuge in fresh water or on land in order to escape dangers in the ocean. Some littoral animals cannot live below certain levels, or they will

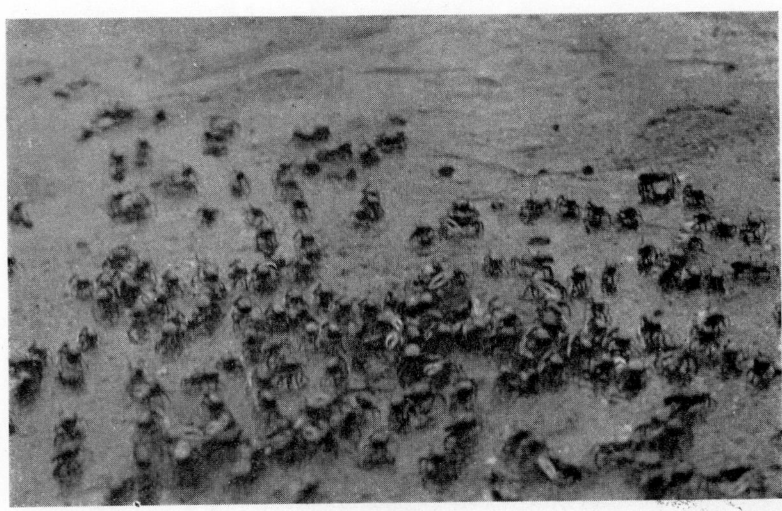

Fig. 10. Fiddler crabs feed above the water at low tide. They fear enemies in the ocean.

be devoured by predaceous enemies (Huntsman, 1918a). Estuaries and swamps have been looked upon by some writers (Hesse, 1920; Annandale, 1922) as refuges where primitive and archaic types may persist after they have been driven from the ocean. Examples of animals cited as those which have thus persisted in fresh water are hydras, certain crabs, and ganoid fishes.

There are marine animals which fear the sea. For example, the fiddler and macrophthalmid crabs which live in the intertidal zone never feed when their burrows are covered with water. They browse about in great armies over exposed beaches, but when the tide rises, each crab retreats into its burrow, plugs up the opening, and remains safe inside until the water recedes again. On rough eroded beaches, like those on the shores of Bermuda and Japan, little snails without shells (Onchidium) live in the crevices. These never come out to feed when the tide covers their homes (Arey & Crozier, 1921;

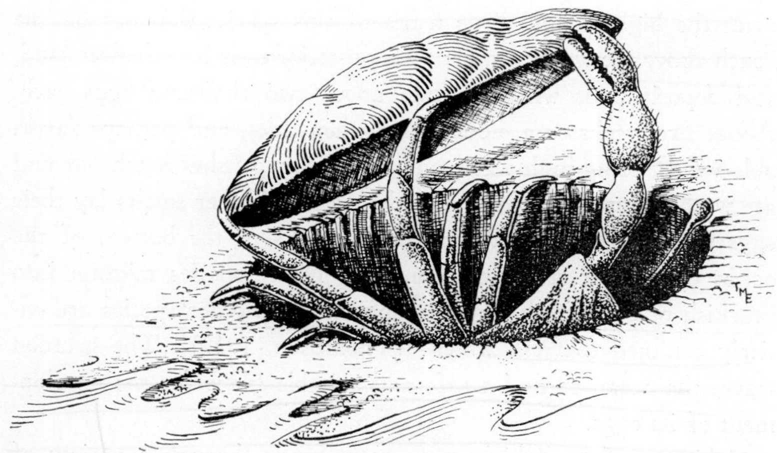

Fig. 11. When the rising tide is about to cover the mouth of a fiddler crab's burrow the owner digs a plug and closes the mouth until the tide recedes again.

Pearse, 1931a). The burrowing crustacean which is often called the beach flea (Talorchestia), though it lives a semi-terrestrial life along the shore and has little or no toleration for fresh water, avoids the sea (Verwey, 1927). The ghost crab (Ocypode) lives in a burrow on land and commonly hides by throwing sand over its body so that nothing but its stalked eyes protrude (Cowles, 1908). It commonly hunts along sandy beaches at night. If it is then pursued, it may dash into the ocean for a short time but does not stay long. At Tortugas a common predaceous fish, the gray snapper, devours the ghost crab whenever it can.

Johnstone (1908) suggests that salmon were originally marine fishes and that they have developed the habit of spawning in fresh water in order to protect their eggs from marine enemies. On the California coast there is a remarkable smelt, the grunion, *Leuresthes tenuis* (Ayers). This fish comes out on sandy beaches on moonlight nights during March, April, and May to lay its eggs. Just after the highest tides little fishes of this species flop out on the beach above the water, wiggle their posterior ends into the wet sand, and deposit pods which contain about two thousand eggs each. About two weeks or a month later when tides, and perhaps favorable winds, bring high water again, the young fishes hatch out and are washed out of the sand into the ocean. "Other smelts lay their eggs very differently, attached to the rocks or the bottom of the ocean by slender stalks or filaments. Many species migrate into brackish or even fresh water to spawn, while other species are entirely confined to fresh water" (Thompson, 1919). The grunion leaves the ocean to find a safe and suitable place for the development of its eggs.

Gobies are fishes which as a group range through a variety of habitats from littoral waters to torrential mountain streams, and a few are pelagic and bathybial. Certain of them are beach skippers. These fishes live near water but show considerable reluctance to enter it. If pursued they skip on top of the water, climb the roots of mangroves, hide among thick vegetation, but seldom plunge beneath the surface or swim (Pearse, 1928a, 1933). The eyes of beach-skipping gobies are adjusted for far vision in the atmosphere, and thus differ from those of most fishes.

Among the enemies that threaten animals in any habitat are parasites. The geographic distribution of parasites and their hosts may be used to indicate the past history and relationships of animals (Metcalf, 1929). Ward (1910) made a careful study of the parasites of various species of salmon in an attempt to determine whether they showed marine or fresh-water affinities. He found that European salmon were infested largely with marine parasites, but that those along American shores carried mostly parasites that they had acquired in fresh water. The results were therefore not very conclusive. Trematodes belonging to the family Heterophytidae occur in both the ocean and in fresh water. Stunkard & Shaw (1931) have shown that some species in this family can complete their life cycles in sea water or in nearly fresh water.

The vermillion spotted newt *Triturus viridescens* Rafinesque passes through two phases during its life cycle. In its aquatic phase it carries more parasites than in its terrestrial phase (Holl, 1932). In Japan the parasites of eight species of salamanders were studied (Pearse, 1932f). Some parasites were found only in aquatic and others only in terrestrial hosts. On the whole there was little difference between the two types, except for cases due to host specificity. Acanthocephalans and trypanosomes were found only in aquatic hosts, which may seem natural, but it is hard to understand why opalinid and flagellate parasites were found only in terrestrial types.

At Tortugas the distribution of the parasites of crustaceans was studied (Pearse, 1929, 1930a, 1932c). Most species of parasites occurred in the intertidal zone, but most individual parasites were found in hosts that lived on land. Epistylis, nematodes, barnacles, copepods, isopods, rotifers, mites, and fly larvae occur as parasites or commensals in the gills of crabs. At Tortugas and on the coasts of China and Japan (Pearse, 1930a, b, 1931, 1932f) more parasites were found in the gills of land crabs than in those of aquatic crabs, but this was not true at the mouth of the Menam in Siam (Pearse, 1933a), where numerous barnacles lived in the branchial chambers of certain species. In Siam and India more parasites were found associated with aquatic than with land fishes (Pearse, 1932a).

There are many valid instances of animals which have left the ocean to escape various dangers. However, there appears to be no instance where an animal has migrated from the ocean to fresh water or land to escape parasites. Most plants and animals which attack animals as parasites associate themselves with their hosts insidiously. There are some exceptions to this rule. Parts of Africa have been depopulated by tsetse flies; the caribou migrate north in summer in attempting to escape swarms of mosquitoes and warble

Fig. 12. Two gobies resting on the roots of mangroves (Rhizophora) in a Nigerian estuary. When disturbed these fish do not dive but skip on the surface of the water to another root.

flies. Parasites may at times be a factor in exterminating hosts in particular habitats, but they have apparently not played an important rôle along seashores or the borders of bodies of freshwater in causing hosts to change habitats.

Toleration Ranges; Resistance

Animals that live along the transition zones between land and water or between salt water and fresh water are often subject to sudden and extreme variations in environmental conditions, and some of them have become quite resistant to such fluctuations. In their relations to aboceanic migrations the toleration of animals to certain changes in environmental factors will be considered.

Allee (1923a, b) and Prenant & Teissier (1924) have made rather careful studies of the distribution of littoral animals in relation to environmental factors. Allee, who worked on the coast of Massachusetts, concludes that the character of the bottom is perhaps more important than any other factor. The complex of factors which accompany muddy bottoms are radically different from those which obtain on rocky beaches. Prenant & Tessier made observations on the coast of France, with special reference to sessile barnacles, bryozoans, and hydrozoans. They found that the action of strong waves and currents favored the growth of several species of barnacles. Some species endured fresh water well, others did not. One species of barnacle flourished where there was much sediment in the water. Desiccation was fatal to some species but well endured by others. Similar observations were made concerning the tolerations of bryozoans and hydroids. The animals studied by Prenant & Teissier, being sessile, were not such as have been invaders of the land. In fact, few of such types have even attained life in fresh water. The seashore appears to be conducive on the whole to a vast number of individuals of enduring, resisting, unprogressive types. Along with these are a few active, more progressive animals which have generally led the way out of the ocean. Among the latter, ability to stand extreme or varying environmental conditions is one quality that permits the taking up of new modes of life.

It is a primary ecological principle that types of animals which are found in many kinds of habitats have wide ranges of toleration for environmental conditions. The larvae of ephydrid flies live in brine that is much saltier than the ocean, in urine, alkaline solutions, oils, and other media which would be fatal to most animals.

"This ability appears to be due to the presence of a very impermeable cuticle and a very efficient mechanism of hairs and bristles protecting the spiracular openings" (Thorpe, 1931). In the oil vats in California, fly larvae subsist on organic food which consists largely of the bodies of dead insects. In the vats their intestines are full of crude oil, which, however, does not come in contact with living cells. Adult ephydrid flies walk about on oil without being injured.

"A characteristic feature of living organisms is the possession of mechanisms which protect them against the effects of changes of their environments.

"These mechanisms in their earlier forms exert their action by restricting the interchange which they allow between the organism and its surroundings. As they develop in efficiency, they become more selective in action, and are able to preserve the essential characters of the organism while allowing a free interchange with its environment. They have preserved, even in the higher organisms, some of the conditions of cell life which probably existed at very early stages of their evolution.

"As the complexity of organisms has increased, they have rendered themselves more independent of their external environment by providing their cells with an immediate environment of their own. By this means external changes are only allowed to reach the cells in a modified form. The possession of this internal environment enables the organism to obtain the advantages of a freer interchange with its surroundings without endangering the stability of its essential living matter.

"The evolutionary development of the adaptive mechanisms of the organism has continually extended the range and scope of its control over its environment. . . . As the effectiveness of the mechanisms of the environment to its needs has increased, the need for further adaptive modification of the organism has correspondingly diminished" (Wardlaw, 1931).

The toleration of animals for variations in salinity, osmotic pressure, gravity, temperature, water, light, food, gases, molar agents, and ionization will be briefly considered in the following pages.

Salinity

Many animals that had their origin in the ocean can endure salinities below that of sea water, and numerous animals that first came into existence on land have taken up life in the sea. Such typically marine animals as the corals that live in the tropics readily tolerate a reduction of 20% in the salinity of the waters in which they live (Vaughan, 1919). The brine shrimp *Artemia salina* (L.) may live in water which ranges from fresh to that which is much saltier than the ocean, and its eggs will also develop in a wide range of salinities (Sciacchitano, 1927). Several marine algae live when transferred directly from the ocean to fresh water (Chater, 1927). Various worms, mollusks, and king crabs readily withstand considerable dilutions of sea water (Pearse, 1928). The fresh-water Rumanian lakes contain a mixture of marine and fresh-water types (Borcea, 1931), and the former have apparently slowly migrated in from the ocean.

Finley (1930) studied the survival of fifty species of protozoans when transferred directly from fresh water to sea water and found that several species were not injured by such treatment. *Tetramitus salinus* (Entz) lives in salinities of 11% to 15%; *Rhizophora salina* Kirby, in 34.8% where the pH is 9.48 (Kirby, 1932). The pulmonate snail *Physa heterostropha* (Say) remains active in a medium to which sea water is gradually added until the mixture contains 25% of sea water, but beomes inactive at 35 to 40%, and dies in higher salinities (Richards, 1929a). No insects live continually in salinities higher than 2.5%, except dipterous larvae and a larval caddis-fly on the coast of New Zealand (Buxton, 1926), though various bugs live on the surface of the open sea and on the brine in salt vats (Hutchinson, 1931). At Tortugas dragon-fly nymphs survived in water which had gradually grown more salty by evaporation up to more than 6% (Pearse, 1932e).

The aquatic insects of the most specialized groups (Diptera, Coleoptera) are generally more resistant to high salinities than those of more primitive groups (Thorpe, 1927). In the salty ponds in Californa, Diptera occur in the highest concentrations and Coleoptera and Trichoptera in somewhat lower ones (Thorpe, 1931). Natural salty waters do not all serve as the same type of habitats as sea water, even though their salinities or densities may be similar. For example, a rotifer, *Branchionus mulleri* Ehrenberg, lives in a variety of saline waters including the ocean. Rotifers of this species collected in a pond in Nebraska where salinity was 4.5% thrived in artificial sea water which had a salinity of 3.2% but did not flourish as well as in the same medium which had a salinity of 4.5%. They were little affected by calcium-free sea water and lived in alkaline solutions having salinities of 0.57% to 9.05%. They were unable to live in solutions which contained only one salt (Worley, 1929). In certain African lakes rotifers and fishes were the only animals which were found to live in high salinities or alkalinities (Beadle, 1932a).

Sea water is a balanced medium, and each ion or radical may have a more or less specific effect on organisms that live in it, or may change the character of the medium as a habitat. Breder (1933) says, "Field and laboratory studies have indicated that Ca has a protective value to marine teleosts against the effects of the lower tonicity of fresh water." Marine fishes have often invaded waters which contained calcium, even when little sodium was present. Breder tried experiments in aquaria and found that several marine species were able to live in fresh water to which calcium salts had been added. On the other hand, Thorpe (1932) maintains that the general absence of insects from the sea is not due to lack of available calcium. He has found insects in waters where the salinity was higher than the ocean but in which there was little calcium. The

Caspian Sea contains more calcium than the ocean and is less saline, but insects have not migrated into it in unusual numbers. Calcium salts in the ocean are important in maintaining the alkali reserve and thus prevent the activities of organisms from producing local acidity (Bruce, 1928). In sea water sodium, magnesium, and potassium as sulphates or chlorides do not affect carbon dioxide pressure materially, but phosphates may do so to some extent, and carbonates have very marked effects (Shelford, 1929).

Respiration in sea water is much easier than in fresh water (Prenant, 1929). The oxygen requirements of fresh-water animals are greater, probably because they have to expend more energy in maintaining osmotic equilibrium with the surrounding medium. Changes in salt concentration in external or internal media change the rate of respiration in many marine animals (Schlieper, 1929a; Borsuk & Kreps, 1929; Beadle, 1931). In marine animals which cannot adjust themselves to fresh water, respiration may decrease or cease altogether in lowered salinities (Shoup, 1932). Carbonates help respiration by taking up carbon dioxide (Harms, 1929).

Aquatic animals are generally better able to stand slow than rapid changes in salinity (Schlieper, 1933). Marine animals show toleration for varying degrees of dilution according to the concentration of the medium in which they have lived previously (Federighi, 1931). Such adaptations may exert profound changes in the whole configuration of an animal. The brine shrimp *Artemia salina* (L.) has different forms which are correlated with various salinities. Certain littoral snails are smaller in water of greater salinity and larger in lower salinities (Metcalf, 1930). Teleost fishes, in which body fluids are not isotonic with the surrounding medium, change weight and the salinity of their body fluids when the salinity of the surrounding medium changes. Most marine fishes if placed suddenly in fresh water die, probably on account of loss of essential salts (Sumner, 1906; Chassion, 1930) or increased difficulty in respiration (Schlieper, 1929), but a few species are able to survive.

Many animals when transferred directly from the ocean into air or fresh water live longer in the former than in the latter (Borradaile, 1903; Pearse, 1929; Barnes, 1932). According to their toleration for varying salinities aquatic animals may be classified as stenohalin or euryhalin (Schlieper, 1933). The former are limited to narrow ranges, and the latter endure various salinities. Not all animals fall sharply into one class or the other (Beadle, 1932a), but there are species or even individuals in a single species which have intermediate tolerations. Nearly related marine species, as the worms in the genus Nereis, may have quite different degrees of toleration for fresh water; young individuals may differ markedly from old individuals of the same species. Some species have narrowly restricted optima; others can change their organization so as to carry on their activities without difficulty through a wide range of salinities. Along the shores of Puget Sound the species of barnacles on the shore indicate the degree of salinity. Some of the species are larger and more definitely divided into zones in high salinities but in low salinities are smaller and less sharply segregated (Rice, 1930). Along the coast of Japan the eggs of each species of oyster require peculiar conditions of salinity for optimum development. Littoral oysters are euryhalin; brackish-water species are adapted to low salinities; and a sublittoral species is stenohalin (Amemiya, 1928). Plants along the seashore show rather definite segregation in relation to the salinity of the water (Gessner, 1931).

Reproductive activities are often related to or limited by salinity. The Baltic Sea contains less salt than most oceans. Some adult marine animals are able to persist, but their offsprings cannot mature; others have been favored by low salinity. For example, local species of Nereis and Cyanea have increased in numbers, and Aurelia has decreased (Reibisch, 1926). The eggs of Nereis and other littoral animals may be fertilized and may develop in greatly diluted sea water, but the eggs of such a stenohalin type as Echinarachnius will not survive such treatment (Just, 1930, 1930a). Cannon

(1923) observed the effects of salinity on the development of a tropical land crab, *Cardisoma armatum* Herklots. He took eggs from a single female and found that in sea water they hatched into healthy larvae; in fresh water some eggs burst the shell, but no larvae lived; in a mixture of half sea water and half fresh water some eggs hatched and produced apparently normal larvae. In Siam, Alexander (1932) studied the adults of a fresh-water crab (*Paratelphusa* sp.). Individuals stood direct transfer from fresh water to sea water, but died in solutions of sugar which were much below the sea in density. He concluded that electrolytes in the medium were essential.

Many aquatic animals are able to discriminate slight changes in salinity and respond in such ways that they usually survive. Oysters are sensitive to slight variations and cease to feed when salinities fall below certain limits, which are characteristic for each species (Amemiya, 1928; Nelson, 1928). Fishes are quite sensitive to slight changes in the salt content of the water in which they live (Johnstone, 1908; Shelford & Powers, 1915; Wells, 1915). The euryhalin killifish or top-minnow *Fundulus heteroclitus* (L.) is able to distinguish toxic from non-toxic salts, but "variations in temperature or in stream flow profoundly influence the reactions and are more powerful factors in the behavior of the fish than the 'presence or absence of salinity' " (Chidester, 1922). Aquatic animals which are placed in solutions that are hypo- or hyper-tonic to the medium in which they have lived may die from various causes. In their ability to resist the effects of changes which may be induced by immersion in fluids which differ in osmotic pressure from those within their bodies animals fall into three groups: (1) those which have external membranes which offer little or no resistance to the passage of water and solutes; (2) those which have semipermeable external membranes that permit water to pass freely but restrict or do not allow solutes to pass; and (3) those which have essentially impermeable external membranes (Pike & Scott, 1915; Hukuda, 1932). Examples of these are: (1) marine invertebrates in which the salt content of the body fluids is much like that of sea water in which they live, i.e., they are isotonic and isohalin with the surrounding medium; (2) the elasmobranchs (in which body fluids have the same osmotic pressure as sea water, but contain different salts, and in which the density of the blood is maintained by large amounts of urea) and such animals as earthworms, fishes, and frogs which contain body fluids that differ more or less in concentration and composition from the surrounding medium but are influenced by changes in it; and (3) reptiles, birds, and mammals which differ markedly from the surrounding medium and are little influenced by changes in it (Adolph, 1925).

Death in an unsuitable medium may be due to lack of ability to adjust the body fluids so that they are in equilibrium with the medium, to the toxic action of solutes, to the loss of essential salts, to inability to carry on processes such as respiration which are essential for metabolism, or to other causes. Hayes (1930) found that Paramecium reared in culture media did not flourish when salinity produced by adding sea water reached 1% or more. "The animals reacted to changes in salinity in at least four ways: alteration in body shape, change in volume, variation in proportion of water, and deviation from normal rate of respiration. The rate of consumption decreased with increasing salinity to the point of isotonicity, after which respiration increased; the curve was thus U-shaped." Quigley (1928) tested the effects of various substances on a shark, *Squalus suckleyi* (Girard), chiefly by varying the proportion of salts present in sea water. He found that the addition of NaCl, KCl, or CaCl to sea water was not very toxic but that "the most toxic solution was sea water with added salts." Cessation of respiration usually occurred before the heart stopped beating. Koidsumi (1928) investigated the effects of sea water on certain fresh-water chironomid larvae and found that sea water was rapidly fatal, though there are other species of chironomids which regularly live in the ocean.

Barnes (1932) studied the littoral terrestrial isopod *Ligia baudiniana* (Milne-Edwards). He found that solutions of single ions commonly present in sea water were toxic in the following order K, Mg, Ca, Na. Rapid death in such a solution as KCl he believed to be due to inhibition of respiratory movements. He concluded that death in dilute sea water is due to the loss of essential salts rather than injurious osmotic changes. Schlieper (1929) has shown that certain marine animals are actively homoiosmotic in diluted sea water, i.e., they work to maintain their body fluids at certain densities by excreting water. In the shore crab *Carcinas maenas* (Pennant) the intensity of respiration is related to the salinity of the surrounding medium and the crab is able to stand considerable dilution. The shore mussel *Mytilus edulis* L., on the other hand, cannot keep up the molecular concentration of its blood in low dilutions and dies, probably from the effects of asphyxiation. Fresh-water clams have a low salt concentration in their body fluids, but such salts as they have are essential, and their loss results in death (Ellis, Merrick, and Ellis, 1930). The oxygen consumption of barnacles in air depends upon the salt concentration of their body fluids (Borsuk and Kreps, 1929).

Schlieper (1929) maintains that in fresh-water animals, as well as in marine, salinity of blood is related to rate of respiration. When animals are not able to maintain their respiratory activities in changed media they die. Keyes (1931) has studied the survival of the minnow *Fundulus heteroclitus* (L.) in relation to salinity of water and asphyxiation. He separated his fishes into two groups, those that died quickly and those that lived longer, and found that they differed in metabolic rate. A slow-living fish survives asphyxiation better than one which has a rapid rate; a rapid-living marine fish usually lives in fresh water better. The mechanism for the regulation of such activities is probably concerned with electrolyte equilibria. The oxygen consumption of a marine fish that has been placed in fresh water decreases for a time, but gradually returns to normal if the fish can live. Salts and water leave the body of a fish through its gills in dilute solutions, and the loss of essential salts may thus cause death (Sumner, 1906). In marine invertebrates and elasmobranchs osmotic swelling is proportional to the diminution of the osmotic pressure of the blood (Hukuda, 1932). Changes in weight and salt content take place in teleost fishes when the salinity of the medium varies, but they are not directly proportional. "The osmotic pressure of the internal medium fluctuates within a much narrower range than that of the external medium" (Sumner, 1906).

Osmotic pressure is like solution pressure of a dissolving solid, vapor tension of an evaporating liquid, or gaseous pressure of a permanent gas. Each molecule goes as fast and as far as it can. Osmosis exerts uniform pressure in a confined space. It is of course modified by ionization, adsorption, electrical conditions, etc. In a living organism a change in osmotic pressure indicates that work is being done in a cell. The body fluids of animals may be maintained in equilibrium with the environment by the kidneys (Hawthorne, 1930; Schlieper, 1929a), or they may be regulated by some other "active living process" (Margaria, 1931).

"The action of all the mechanisms which regulate the chemical relations of the organism is essentially to control the exchange of material which takes place between the organism and its surroundings. In its crudest form this mechanism acts simply by abolishing interchange between organism and environment when the characters of the latter become unsuitable. . . . The differences observable among different species of fish are due to the fact that they possess adjusting mechanisms of different degrees of efficiency and not to the maintenance of specifically distinct levels of osmotic pressure" (Wardlaw, 1931). The changes that animals have undergone to become adapted to various salinities will be considered in the next chapter.

Gravity and Molar Agents

Gravity is in some respects to be regarded as a factor which is unfavorable to the migration of animals from water to land. The specific gravity of many animals is little greater than that of water. Motile aquatic animals therefore have little difficulty in remaining suspended in the medium in which they live, but those that have taken up life on land live in the atmosphere, and their bodies are much heavier than it.

Terrestrial animals burrow in soil, drag their heavy bodies over the surface of the earth, or have more or less effective and special means for support and locomotion. If they ascend elevations, they may be subject to injury from rapid falls and violent collisions with the surface of the earth. A land animal must, if it is to attain any degree of dominance in terrestrial habitats, have skeletal and locomotor structures which support it against the pull of gravity and give it ability to move fast enough to compete with other species. A jellyfish can never become established on land. Gravity in a general way limits the size of land animals. Perhaps the ideal terrestrial types are such animals as active flying insects, swift lizards, agile birds, and saltatorial mice. But some types of land animals, like dinosaurs and elephants, have successfully overcome gravity and attained gigantic size. To do this they consume great quantities of food, which has its ultimate source in land vegetation and sunlight.

Gravitational forces are responsible for the tides which exert such a profound influence on littoral plants and animals. The rhythmical ebb and flow of the ocean along shore alternately exposes animals on beaches twice each day to the influence of the atmosphere and sea water. Intertidal animals therefore develop a certain degree of resistance to the desiccating action of air and the extreme and rapid variations in temperature which are more or less characteristic of terrestrial habitats.

Perhaps some littoral animals have through such influences been

transformed from marine into terrestrial types (Flattely, 1920, 1921; Fulton, 1921), but most sessile intertidal animals tend to be radially symmetrical, resisting rather than alert, and unprogressive (Hayes, 1927; Pearse, 1914, 1922), so that few of them through the ages have gone across beaches to land. The tide offers a reward to animals which can establish themselves above high-tide mark. This is the accumulations along the drift line—the flotsam and jetsam of the sea, which furnish food and shelter.

Molar agents in the form of currents, winds, and waves may bring food to littoral animals, transport species to new localities and thus permit them to obtain a foothold, and produce changes in littoral waters which perhaps at times lead to adaptation which help fit animals for terrestrial life. The faunas on wave-washed beaches or on current-swept shores where there are few waves are similar (Fischer, 1927); littoral water in motion has some similar effects, whether it is in the form of waves or currents. The pounding of waves during storms makes it impossible for some animals to live on exposed shores, and the wetting of higher ground by spray at such times makes it possible for marine animals to become established temporarily on land surfaces or in little pools. Where tides are strong they have rather uniform effects on the littoral water in relation to such qualities as content of O_2 and H_2S, pH, salinity, temperature, and turbidity (Miller, Ramage, & Lazier, 1928), but where they are feeble or erratic this is not true (Moberg, 1927). Winds help flying fishes to leave the ocean for short sails

Fig. 13. A beach near Port Antonio in Jamaica. The rocks serve as homes for crabs and snails, some of which wander into the humid shade of the forest; the wet sand teems with amphipods, isopods, crabs insects, and many other animals; and the lagoon is the home of fishes, sea urchins, jellyfishes, and other swimming or floating life. (Photo by R. E. Blackwelder.)

through the air, but none of these animals has become established on land. The absence of molar agents may have profound effects on aquatic animals, chiefly through the stagnation of water, which causes animals to die or take up breathing from or through the surface of the water.

Temperature

In aquatic habitats there are certain inherent advantages and disadvantages that are associated with temperature. As water grows warmer it can hold less gas in solution and more of most salts. Polar oceans therefore contain an abundance of oxygen for respiratory needs and lack available lime, but animals in shallow tropical waters often produce calcareous deposits and at times find breathing difficult. The rate of metabolism in poikilothermic animals is influenced markedly by temperature. An aquatic animal which lives in a tropical puddle therefore may often lack sufficient oxygen, especially at night when photosynthesis is not replenishing that which is used up by the metabolic activities of organisms. If such an animal gradually becomes adapted to breathing air and is thus able to spend more or less time actually out of water, it meets new dangers in the way of temperature changes, for in any latitude such variations are wider and more rapid on land than in water. Land temperatures, according to Johnstone (1908), may vary between -90°C. and + 65°C.; sea temperatures, -2.8°C. to + 31°C. This gives a range of 155°C. for land and of 33.8°C. for sea. Probably Johnstone's range for the ocean is too limited, but there is no doubt that land temperatures are much more variable than those in water. The specific heat of water is great, and aquatic habitats therefore change temperatures slowly.

Poikilothermic animals live longer at low temperatures, and this fact in part accounts for the abundant populations on the bottoms of some cold oceans and the preponderance of plankton organisms in polar as compared to tropical seas. Oysters live shorter lives at higher temperatures (Hori, 1928). Shelford (1929) has suggested that each type of animal requires a certain characteristic number of thermal units to complete its life.

The survival or the abundance of an animal in a particular habitat may depend upon the extremes that temperatures reach. Many animals can withstand temperatures below the freezing point of water, but few live above about 40° C. At Naples the death of various marine animals was found to occur at temperatures ranging from 32.5° C. to 43.5° C.; variations probably being due to chemical and physical differences between species (Vernon, 1899). Most animals can change their upper limits of temperature toleration somewhat by acclimatization (Hathaway, 1927). At Tortugas some marine and fresh-water animals live in ponds where temperatures reach 42° C. or more (Pearse, 1932e). On the New England coast high temperatures which intertidal barnacles tolerate range from 23.4 to 27° C. (Cole, 1929). Tropical marine animals live near their maximum limits of temperature toleration, and their activities are readily retarded by cold (Mayer, 1914, 1918). When they die at high temperatures it is apparently on account of acidosis and lack of oxygen to carry on metabolic activities.

The faunas of hot springs are derived from fresh water and land. Typically marine animals are absent. "Furthermore the preponderance of species related to ones that have migrated into a marine or semi-marine (brackish) environment indicate that thermal and saline situations have imposed similar obstacles to the biota which has entered them from fresh water. These depend undoubtedly upon the presence of salts in solution and the attendant rise in osmotic pressure of the medium. High temperature is a deterrent that has been overcome by acclimatization ordinarily, however, within quite narrow limits, especially in case of animals, which are able to endure much less heat than plants. An added inconvenience is the rather consistent dearth of dissolved oxygen in thermal waters, which renders respiration more difficult for purely aquatic animals" (Brues, 1927). Most of the inhabitants of hot springs are air breathers. The rat-tailed maggot (*Eristalis*), for example, is quite characteristic. Its jointed, telescoping breathing tube reaches to the surface and permits the inspiration of air.

There are two types of animals which have left the ocean on account of temperature influences. Some euryhalin animals like the salmon, ciscoes, and certain crustacean relicts, which spawn on the pebbly bottoms near the headwaters of streams (Chidester, (1924) or now live permanently in the cool, profundal regions of deep lakes, are little limited in their environmental relations by variations in salinity but are associated primarily with cold water. These animals have spread from the ocean whenever there was opportunity. A nice illustration of the dependence of ciscoes on low temperatures is given by Fry (1937). In Lake Nipissing they move from shallow to deep water in summer and remain until lack of oxygen forces them near or above the thermocline. They feed less and grow less in deep water. The other type of animals has left the ocean, invaded fresh water, and then been forced to take up life on land in the tropics, where high temperatures make metabolism of poikilothermic animals rapid and thus increase oxygen requirements where the oxygen content of the water is often low and the atmosphere often humid. This combination of factors makes respiration in shallow fresh waters difficult and permits life on land without great danger of desiccation and loss of activity on account of low temperatures.

Adaptations which enable animals to live on land at low or high temperatures may be concerned with bodily temperature regulation, the prevention of water loss, water storage, or the assumption of torpid states. Hibernating insects are prepared for low temperatures by the increase in bound water in their bodies (Robinson, 1928), or, what perhaps amounts to the same thing, a decrease in free water (Bodine, 1923). Mammals also prepare for hibernation by loss of water from their blood (Rasmussen, 1917). Insects survive longest in dry air at high temperatures when they can cool their bodies by evaporation; this means that only insects of some size can live under such conditions, and that small insects are confined to moist, cool situations (Mellanby, 1932). Frogs which have the subdermal spaces full of water can remain some time in the atmosphere, but such a reserve of water is soon exhausted and must then be renewed. A desert lizard is well insulated against the loss of water and adapted to high temperatures.

WATER

Aquatic habitats differ from those on land in that they show no change corresponding to humidity. The ability of many types of animals to live on land is dependent to a considerable degree on the amount of water present in the atmosphere or soil. Water vapor is lighter than air in the ratio of 5 to 8, and damp air is therefore lighter than dry air. Air has 1/800 the density of water. It takes 4 to 5 times as much heat to raise air 1° C. as to heat dry soil the same amount (Fowler, 1928). Some animals absorb water; others lose it at all temperatures. Most insects have an optimum humidity that is little below saturation (Ludwig, 1945); many are therefore nocturnal or become dormant when moisture decreases. Desert animals have special adaptations for acquiring and conserving water.

"The necessity of water in biologic processes is universal" (Rountree, 1922). Water not only furnishes material for building living substance but aids in solution, circulation, oxidation, hydration, hydrolysis, lubrication, excretion, and other activities. Every animal must have a continual supply of water to carry on its life processes. If water cannot be obtained in free form, it must be acquired from food or even by the breaking down of the tissues of the organism that uses it.

Animals along the seashore are adjusted to various degrees in regard to their water requirements. Eight species of snails which Colgan (1910) studied on the Irish coast were arranged in rather definite zones between low- and high-tide marks and showed in the same order progressive ability to survive in dry air; their limits ranging from 6 to 42 days. A mud-flat snail (Ilyanassa) from the coast of the United States survived only five days when treated similarly (Dimon, 1905). Two species of beach hoppers (Talorchestia) studied by Verwey (1927) were found to occupy different zones on the beach and to require different amounts of water in the sand in which they lived. Some marine, littoral animals drown in water but must visit the ocean frequently in order to moisten their bodies or their respiratory surfaces. Among these, beach-skipping gobies, fiddler crabs (Uca), and the ghost crabs (Ocypode) may be mentioned. A barnacle, kept out of water for a week or two, goes into a resting state and then will remain alive for some time. Monterosso (1927, 1929) thus kept barnacles alive for from 100 to 140 days. When he submerged them for a short time at intervals of 30 to 90 days, some individuals remained alive for more than two years. Some barnacles which are attached near high-tide mark are usually submerged for only one hour out of twenty (Flattely & Walton, 1922). The little isopod *Ligia exotica,* which runs about near the water on tropical beaches, may live 8 hours to 4 days out of water, depending on temperature and amount of moisture in the atmosphere. In a saturated atmosphere death occurs when 8% of the body weight has been lost. The body contains about 75% of water, and a loss of 10 to 18% is always fatal. This crustacean must live near the sea because, though terrestrial, it has no special water-retaining adaptations. In Java, Harms (1929) found that beach gobies lived only 1 to 5 days on damp mud without water. Three species of blennies live under stones about a meter above and below low-tide mark on the beaches in Puget Sound, Miles (1920) believes because oxygen is more abundant there than in the ocean below.

Animals that are characteristic of swamps, marshes, and pools often have remarkable powers of enduring desiccation. Water mites stand partial desiccation, if covered with dry debris, for 3 to 6 months, but die quickly if exposed in air (Szalay, 1928). An oriental leech lived in a cocoon on dry paper for a week, during which it lost 80% of its weight, and became active in a short time when again immersed in water (Oka, 1922). Frogs and toads cannot absorb water to any extent from a moist atmosphere, but must come in contact with water, soil, or some other wet object to replenish their body losses (Adolph, 1932). Certain air-breathing fishes in India live without water in moist air on wet grass from 5 to 60 hours (Das, 1927). Collembola on account of their small size are usually limited to damp habitats, but those with tracheal tubes are on the whole able to stand desiccation better than those without (Davies, 1928). Certain serpent-head fishes in Siam remain in dry soil in rice fields without water for as much as four months in stiff mud cells (Smith, 1927). Lung-fishes also remain encapsuled in mud cocoons for as long as two years (perhaps sometimes for five years), and urea may accumulate in their bodies until it amounts to as much as 2% of their body weight (Smith, 1930). According to Hubbs, some swamp fishes in North America, (Eucaulia, Umbra, Amia, Ameiurus, etc.), can live for a time in mud. Lung-like cavities were developed in fishes as an adaptation to dry seasons, according to Romer (1945), but the writer believes that such cavities more often originated in decreasing aquatic habitats where there was a lack of oxygen.

Land animals of course all have more or less ability to do without water and some live their whole lives without any free water. The jerboa and gazelle subsist on vegetation and will not drink if water is available (Buxton, 1923). A fasting meal-worm larva (Tenebrio) can keep its body water constant for a month while fasting at temperatures of 23° to 30°C. and humidities of 0% to 60%. "It seems to be able to do this by consuming some stored substance and holding the water produced in metabolism" (Buxton, 1930). A clothes moth (Tinea) can subsist throughout life on nothing but air-dried wool or fur which contains from 3.66% to 9.08% of water, and maintains its body water at 57.66% to 59.83% (Babcock, 1912). The larva of the beetle Trogoderma, which is commonly known as the "museum pest," has lived for more than four years in a small bottle without food, at times molting and devouring its own skin (Wodsedalek, 1917). Argasid ticks may live two to six years as unfed adults, but ixodid ticks usually survive only for six to eight months (Nuttall, 1911).

"The length of time that animals can endure atmospheres of low relative humidity in general depends primarily on the kind of integument and secondly on the proportion of the surface to body mass. Metabolism of an organism is important in its resistance to exsiccation" (Hall, 1922). A man when starved may lose 40% of his body weight, including half of his proteins and nearly all of his glycogen and fat, without serious danger, but the loss of 10% of his water results in serious disorders and of about 20% in death (Rountree, 1922). Shelford (1929) investigated the effects of rapid evaporation produced by air currents, and measured the rate by Livingston porous cups. "The animals killed by rapid evaporation fall into two distinct groups: (a) those dying with an evaporation varying from 0.07 to 5.40 cc. after an exposure varying from 5 to 165 minutes, and (b) those dying with an evaporation of 31.0 to 42.0 cc. after an exposure of 1,300 to 2,220 minutes. The first group was made up of soft skinned amphibians, the second of chitin-covered arthropods. Even though the arthropods were much smaller and hence had much more surface per volume, they lived from 8 to 450 times as long as the amphibians." Littleford, Keller, & Phillips (1947) tested the ability of five species of plethodontid salamanders to endure desiccation and found that they lost 18 to 25.85% of body weight before death. Ability to endure water loss was correlated with habit and habitat. The mucous coating on many littoral algae, snails, and fishes helps such organisms to resist desiccation.

Radiant Energy

Radiant energy exerts profound influences on organisms. It produces chemical changes which are injurious to protoplasm; stimulates or inhibits the activity of protoplasm or of whole organisms; makes possible the perception of distant objects by vision; stimulates formation of pigment, colors, and patterns; activates substances in organisms and foods so that they acquire greater value for nutrition and metabolism; stimulates the activity of endocrine glands; energizes photosynthesis; etc. Laurens (1928) points out that light is *visible* radiant energy and that it is a misnomer to speak of ultra-violet or infra-red *light*. A man perceives radiant energy as light which has ranges between 390$\mu\mu$ and 760$\mu\mu$; a honey bee has a range which extends further into the shorter vibrations. The vibrations which are most effective in causing pigment formation in man are about 300$\mu\mu$ in length; still shorter vibrations cause sunburn.

Radiant energy is absorbed in a selective manner as it passes through water. In a general way the longer wavelengths are eliminated near the surface, and the shorter vibrations penetrate deepest. Penetration may be interfered with by suspended matter, surface disturbances, stains, and other things. Seas are usually clearer than rivers and lakes. In a lumber region the presence of tannin in water cut down the blue light that would normally reach to considerable depths (Shelford, 1929).

Organisms from the ocean may, if they become established on land, gain certain advantages because more radiant energy is available for the manufacture of foods and the furthering of metabolic processes, but they may also suffer from the injurious effects that such energy often produces. In general plants and animals are more or less precisely adjusted to carry on their daily activities in certain

Fig. 14. A sunny pool in Florida where mosquitoes (Uranotaenia) breed. (Photo by R. H. Arnett, Jr.)

ranges. As the radiant energy that is available on the surface of the earth comes largely from the sun and, because of the rotation of the earth on its axis, the supply varies regularly during every twenty-four hours, the activities of many animals are rhythmic. Nocturnal and diurnal animals have energy requirement levels which are adjusted to particular periods in the diurnal cycle. Among common pond fishes in the United States the carp and mud minnow are most often active at night, the pumpkinseed during the day, and the cisco at all hours. Most locusts sing during the day; katydids and tree crickets, at night. Many cave animals live for generations without light. Even mammals, such as horses in mines, appear to remain healthy for years in the absence of sunlight if fed proper food. Many animals have periods of rest and activity which are correlated with the changes in available energy which occur as the earth travels annually about the sun; i.e., seasonal periodicities. There are many examples of what are known as spring, summer, autumn, or winter animals. Life apparently originated in the ocean where all materials which are essential for the building of protoplasm are available in solution. But energy which may be captured and used to activate organisms is much less in submerged marine habitats than in those on land. It is generally true that the most progressive animals have developed where most energy is available. Kennedy (1928) in discussing insects has made it plain that the most specialized and progressive types are active in the habitats and at the times in the daily and annual cycles where and when most radiant energy is available.

In struggling to leave aquatic habitats some animals have apparently been stopped by radiant energy. Direct sunlight kills many marine invertebrates (Huntsmann, 1924), which therefore must remain submerged or leave their homes in water only at night. On the other hand, some littoral plants and animals which have not been able to leave the salty sea are dependent on the abundant light that is found above the water. For example, the common rockweed (Fucus) can grow submerged or out of the water but must have a considerable amount of light. "Light is the controlling factor in determining the lower limit of Fucus" (Gail, 1920).

Food

The advantages of the land in connection with food manufacture have already been discussed (pp. 56-58). In this section it is only necessary to mention briefly the limitations that food as an ecological factor may place on aboceanic migrations.

The food chains, such as that which begins with microscopic floating plants and ends with whales, have been much discussed by oceanographers, and many of them are well known. Most marine animals have a rather stable and ever-present food supply in the water which surrounds them or in the oozy muds which accumulate on the bottom. There are some exceptions to this rule among predaceous marine animals. The black swallower can ingest other fishes which are larger than itself and, as it lives in cool water at considerable depths, probably eats seldom. In fresh water and on land food supplies are more intermittent. Some animals which live in such situations are dependent on foods which may be available only at intervals of days, months, or even years. Correlated with this is the fact that the famous fasters among animals are to be found in fresh water and on land—leeches, ticks, museum pests, etc. In this connection it is again apparent that animals which leave the stable, dependable ocean to live on tide-swept beaches, in fluctuating rivers, swamps, and pools, or in various land habitats must develop resistances which will carry them through lean seasons. They must at times become torpid and merely endure and at times go without food. But on the whole, of course, there are better, more concentrated foods on land than in aquatic habitats.

Conclusions

Animals have left the ocean and invaded fresh-water or land habitats for various causes. Some have been forced to leave on account of respiratory difficulties or enemies in water. Others were perhaps attracted by the foods of high quality that are available in fresh water and on land, or by desirable conditions for breeding. Still others left the ocean without any particular necessity or lure in order to escape competition and occupy an unoccupied environmental niche; they became established on land through natural spreading tendencies, as a result of ecological successions and segregations. In attaining land many types have had to give up old racial traditions. They have been obliged to develop new ranges of toleration and new resistances in relation to environmental conditions. They have left habitats with uniformity, stability, and low energy for those in which variability, instability, and high energy are characteristic. Some animals are "preadapted" for such changes, others make radical modifications in their structure and physiology.

4

HOW THE ANIMALS HAVE CHANGED

THE view that life originated in the ocean has already been set forth. Some great groups have never left the ocean and are confined to it today—Ctenophora, Brachiopoda, Echinodermata, Polychaeta, Cephalopoda, and Tunicata. Three other groups are largely marine; comparatively few representatives of sponges, coelenterates, and bryozoans are found in fresh water. Amphibia are confined almost wholly to fresh water, but a few frogs even breed in brackish water which may contain as much as 2.6% salt (Pearse, 1911). Lung-fishes (Dipnoi) are found only in fresh water. Only two large groups of animals, Myriapoda and Onychophora, are exclusively terrestrial.

No Protozoa are terrestrial. Though many species occur in soils, they are active only when water is present. Some even occur at times on snow. A few flatworms are terrestrial. They are protected from desiccation to some extent by their slimy secretions, but are confined to moist situations and are nocturnal. Nematoid worms occur in the soil in great numbers. Other species are found in or on terrestrial plants. Earthworms are commonly confined to damp soil, but some of them climb trees and lurk in crevices in the bark. Land leeches commonly rest under fallen leaves or other objects along shady pathways and hasten out into the open when a prospective host passes. Among mollusks only gastropods have attained land life. Many marine and river snails are branchiate; littoral and pond snails are commonly pulmonate. Land snails lack gills and use the mantle cavity as a lung; they are protected by a mucous covering and, except in slugs, by a spirally coiled shell, which during quiescent periods may be closed by an operculum. They are commonly nocturnal or crepuscular and are active when the air is humid. Their eggs are laid in the soil or in rotting logs and are protected by tough coverings. Arthropods are protected from desiccation by exoskeletons and thus readily take up temporary or permanent residence on land. In crustaceans which become adapted to terrestrial conditions gills dwindle and organs (tracheae, branchial tufts) develop which permit respiration in moist internal cavities. Excretion through malpighian tubules replaces that through paired metameric kidneys. Insects are dominant land animals and at present share the land habitats with their chief rivals, the vertebrates. Though they originated on land, many have gone into fresh water, and a few types have even become established in the ocean. Noble (1931) has well described the modifications of the vertebrates for terrestrial life as follows:

"If the modern fish were to be changed to a tetrapod, a number of important transformations of structure would have to be accomplished. The gills would have to be lost, and the lungs developed and the nasal passages extended to form internal nares for the ingress of air when the mouth is closed. The fins and body would have to be modified for land locomotion and the integument changed to resist drying. The latter would mean the development of a cornified epidermal covering and a series of integumentary glands discharging by ducts on to the surface, at least over those parts not provided with an armored skin. Special glands would be required to keep the nasal passage and mouth from drying. The eyes, formerly bathed by the water, would be especially sensitive to the new conditions and must either develop a horny, protective cover as in modern snakes or produce softer eyelids out of dermal folds. In either case a lacrimal gland and drain would be needed for cleansing the eyeball. To keep the nasal passage clean a muscular closing device would be required at the outer end of each nasal inlet. If the first tetrapod were to succeed on land, the sense organs of the fish would have to undergo considerable modification, for, while the lateral line organs would be no longer required, the auditory, optic, and olfactory centers would gain a high importance, demanding in some cases fundamental changes in the structure of the organs. If the head were as flat as that of many frogs, special muscles to raise the eyes above the surface of the skull would be needed if the eyes were to be at all efficient. Lastly, the loosely hung jaw of the majority of teleosts would have to be firmly fixed to the brain case."

Land animals have more or less effective, and often elaborate, mechanisms for conserving water, regulating temperature, maintaining internal fluids at optimum concentrations, respiration in air, reproduction without water, and locomotion and sensation in air. How such adaptations have developed will be considered in the following sections.

The following classification of animals in relation to environment is proposed by Harms & Dragendorff (1933):

I. Aquatic Animals: positively hydrotactic.
   a. Passively Homoiosmotic, Stenohaline Animals: marine.
      1. Plankton Animals.
      2. Swimming Animals.
      3. Animals Living on Ground.
      4. Animals Living in Ground.
   b. Passively Poikilosmotic, Euryhaline Animals: little adapted brackish water animals. Classes 1 to 4 as under *a.*
   c. Actively Poikilosmotic, Euryhaline Animals: specifically adapted brackish water animals: Classes 1 to 4 as under *a.*
   d. Actively Poikilosmotic Animals, Euryhaline to Homoiosmotic Animals: estuaries and intertidal zones. Classes 1 to 4 as under *a.*
   e. Actively Homoiosmotic Animals: fresh-water animals, including marine teleosts, dipnoans?, ganoids, selachians, and hemicraniotes. Classes 1 to 4 as under *a.*

II. Air Animals: positively aerotropic.
   a. Actively Poikilosmotic to Actively Homoiosmotic. Animals with Well-Developed Skin Organs to Prevent Desiccation (skin glands); in moist (80-90%) air.
      1. Flying Animals: e.g., flying frog.

2. Animals Running or Jumping on Ground: amphibians, periophthalmids, coenobitas.
3. Animals Living in Ground: Phycosoma, Lycastris, nemerteans, earthworms.

b. Actively Homoiosmotic Animals with Well-developed Skin Organs to Prevent Desiccaton (chitin, horn, imbedded glands): dry air animals which are more or less independent of relative humidity.
1. Flying Animals.
2. Animals Living on the Ground.
3. Animals Living in the Ground.

c. Animals which have Secondarily Returned to Water:
1. Damp Air-Breathers: limnaeids.
2. Animals which have Secondarily taken to Water-breathing: many pulmonates, siphonarians, Ancylus, oncidies, ephemerid larvae.

Integument

The chief functions of animal integuments are protection from blows and parasites; insulation against desiccation and loss of heat; respiration; excretion; regulation of body temperatures; and regulation of interchanges between body fluids and the surrounding medium. In general the skins of terrestrial animals are thicker and less permeable than those of aquatic animals (Hesse, 1920; Noble, 1929; Harms, 1932). Thus they more effectively prevent desiccation and protect internal organs. Many of the animals that live in the ocean have an integument which permits free interchange between body fluids and the surrounding medium. Some marine animals and those that live in fresh water are able to maintain their body fluids at concentrations which differ from the media in which they live. Certain aquatic animals and most land animals are little influenced by the surrounding medium, even when they are wet continually by rains or immersed in water.

Wardlaw (1931) says, "Far from tending to isolate themselves more completely from their surroundings, the most perfectly adapted organisms are those in which the freest interchange is allowed with the environment." There may be some question as to what "perfect adaptation" means, but there is no question that primitive marine animals in general have freer interchange between internal and external fluids than do more specialized fresh-water and land animals. In fresh water it is necessary that liquids be prevented from passing out of the bodies of animals and thus decreasing essential substances, or water must be rapidly eliminated in order to maintain the concentration of internal fluids. Most fresh-water animals readily permit the passage of water from their bodies. A paramecium eliminates water equal to 31 to 700 times its own volume daily (Hesse, 1920), depending on temperatures. There are two primary mechanisms involved in the active regulation of osmotic concentration. The kidney concentration of salt and elimination of large amounts of water are characteristic of stenohaline fresh-water fishes; the elimination of excess salt and conservation of the water by the gills appear to be common to the stenohaline marine teleosts and the euryhaline forms like the eel (Keyes, 1933). Chloride-secreting cells in the skin of fishes may keep internal osmotic pressure down (Keyes & Willmer, 1932), and adrenalin, probably by constricting blood-vessels, may decrease or abolish such activity (Keyes & Bateman, 1932). Adult salmon have salt-secreting cells in their skins, but young salmon in fresh water do not.

Protective integumentary structures may manifest themselves as thickenings or special outgrowths such as scales, feathers, or hairs; chitinous or horny cuticle; bony or horny plates; or glands which form mucus, fat, or other secretions. Hatch (1946) points out the advantages of exoskeletal structures to insects and birds. He states that beetles make up half of all existing insects. They are perhaps best protected from water loss. Pantin (1931) says "the acquisition by an animal of independence from its environment has necessitated increased impermeability of its surface membranes." Kennedy (1927) has discussed the advantages and disadvantages of the exoskeletons of insects in a very illuminating way. He says, "The possession of an exoskeleton makes an animal very sensitive to temperature, moisture, light, but at the same time prevents the same animal from developing the more flexible reaction through thought as man knows it. Thought will be forever prohibited to the insect line because it is conditioned on a large mass of properly organized nervous tissue. The exoskeleton of the insect positively prevents the development of a land insect of over an ounce or two in weight." A complete exoskeleton in arthropods is inimical to the development of a large brain. "Besides the skeleton use, it may have developed as an armor in the water or as a protection on tidal beaches." An exoskeleton gives an insect a certain degree of passive resistance, but, as it is a land animal, limits it to a small size and restricts its "reserves of excess tissues." It is stronger than an endoskeleton, gives great surface for muscle attachments, and is excellent for preventing desiccation. The presence of an exoskeleton has left insects plastic in some respects; e.g., it has permitted the evolution of metamorphoses.

Animals such as certain nematodes and dipterous larvae (Thorpe, 1930; Hinman, 1932) are able to live in media which differ markedly from their own body fluids because the cuticles on the outsides of their bodies are practically impermeable. Animals with such cuticles may be aquatic or terrestrial, and the presence of such protective coverings perhaps is to be looked upon as a fortunate accident which permits their possessors to live in media which would be fatal to less protected animals, rather than adaptations which have developed to fit certain environments.

The respiratory functions of the integument in aquatic habitats are served by various types of more or less elaborate gills. Often these are protected in enclosed cavities through which water circulates. Such cavities may enclose the whole body of an animal, as in certain polychaete worms, clams, ostracods, chironomids, and caddisfly larvae, or merely the respiratory organs, as in shrimps and active snails. In air-breathing and terrestrial animals capillaries are often spread over thin, moist membranes, which cover enclosed branchial outgrowths (Anabas, Birgus, Ocypode) or surround cavities within the animal (vertebrate lungs). When animals live where oxygen is deficient or difficult to obtain, gills or dermal breathing structures are most often present. Harms (1929) in speaking of beach-skipping gobies makes the generalization that the more a fish lives in mud the more vascular is its skin.

In leaving the ocean for fresh water, animals encounter two difficulties which require special abilities or adjustments: (1) respiration is more difficult, and (2) there is danger of loss of essential substances from body fluids to the less dense surrounding water by osmosis. The changes by which the external membranes of animals have been able to meet these will be considered in the next two sections. It is worth while, however, to mention here a few points which bear on the adjustments of the skin in passing from sea water to fresh water. Such changes have been studied extensively by Adolph (1925, 1927a, d, 1943). No fresh-water organism is ever in absolute equilibrium with the environment. Bony fishes in the ocean have body fluids which are hypotonic to sea water. Fishes in fresh water are not very different from those in the ocean, and their body fluids are of course hypotonic to sea water. Marine animals can usually endure variations in the salinity of the medium in which they live better than fresh-water animals. The integument may be nearly perfectly permeable and exercise little or no control over the passage of salts, as in a sea cucumber. Such an animal as an earthworm, a fish, or a frog has some degree of control over the passage of solutes through its skin, kidney, or gill membranes. In earthworms and frogs control appears to be more through the skin than the kidneys (Adolph, 1927a, b).

In migrating from the ocean, animals with an exoskeleton or more or less impermeable external membranes have marked advantages over those which can exercise little or no control over the passage of fluids into or out of their bodies. They are able to keep their body fluids in more or less steady state, and their cells continually have a favorable medium for metabolic activities. An animal with a hard or impervious external covering has special advantages on land—the chief colonizers have been arthropods, snails, and vertebrates. The permeability of a tadpole's skin decreases when it metamorphoses into a frog. The skin becomes a better protective mechanism for impeding the passage of solutes. On land it must also retard desiccation. This usually does not facilitate respiration, and breathing in land animals is usually carried on in internal cavities where respiratory membranes may be kept more or less moist without much loss of water. Furthermore, terrestrial amphibians can survive a greater loss of body water than aquatic types (Thorson & Svihla, 1943).

Respiration

The percentage of oxygen in the earth's atmosphere is greater and more constant than in natural waters. This compensates to some extent for the dangers that land animals endure from desiccation and variable temperatures. It is also true that respiration for an aquatic animal is easier in saline than non-saline water (Prenant, 1929). This has probably impeded the migration of certain marine types into fresh water.

Baldwin (1937) gives an excellent discussion of the changes in respiration when animals left the ocean and took up life in fresh water and on land. Respiration must supply oxygen and also get rid of carbon dioxide. "Considerable modifications in respiratory organs became necessary when animals left an aquatic in favor of a terrestrial environment. The advantages to be gained thereby included the exchange of a relatively poor oxygen supply for a very rich one. But respiration has always remained essentially aquatic. The respiratory epithelium, whether it be that of a gill or a lung, is always covered by a stationary aqueous layer. . . . The relative inefficiency of the respiratory organ has been made good by an increase in the area of the respiratory epithelium per unit of body weight in air-breathing animals." There has also been an increase in their vascularization.

Respiration is essentially the same process in air as in water, and in the ocean as in fresh water. Colosi (1927, 1930) has also emphasized the fact that organisms in passing from aquatic to atmospheric media do not change their respiratory medium, since in all terrestrial animals it consists of "a film of aqueous liquid" that moistens the respiratory surfaces and "serves as a path for oxygenation." This "constancy of the respiratory medium" permits migration, during ontogeny or phylogeny, from aquatic to terrestrial environments "without the violent physiological crisis which would accompany an excessive change in oxygen pressure." All organs take their oxygen for respiration from one medium—water. "The physiology of respiration in fishes is the same as in lung-breathing animals" (Powers *et al.*, 1932). In man air which enters at 25° C. and has a humidity of 35%, attains a humidity of 79% in the nose, and of 95 to 98% in the lung (Perwitzschky, 1927). Poikilothermic animals use about the same amount of oxygen per gram per hour as those which live in the ocean at the same temperature (Gjaja, 1922). The rate of metabolism is about the same in reptiles, amphibians, and crustaceans, but in insects and homoiothermic vertebrates it is faster (Krogh, 1916). Poikilothermic animals need less oxygen at low temperatures (Helff & Stubblefield, 1929), though many show seasonal variations (Dolk & Postma, 1927). Some poikilotherms, at least, require less oxygen in salt water than in fresh water (Fox & Simmons, 1933; Schlieper, 1933). The oxygen consumption of barnacles in air depends on the salinity of their body fluids (Borsuk & Kreps, 1929). The alkali reserves in the bloods of animals affect ability to respire in various media. "A series of animals arranged according to their alkali reserve suggests strongly the gradual transition from aquatic to terrestrial life" (Kokubo, 1930).

Marine fishes differ among themselves in ability to live in water containing little oxygen and in respiratory rate. A toadfish (Opsanus) will remove practically all the oxygen from the water around it, but a scup (Stenotomus) dies of suffocation when the oxygen tension is still high (Hall, 1929). However, the rate of oxygen consumption of a fish is lowered by a decrease in the oxygen tension or an increase in the carbon dioxide tension of the surrounding water; and a combination of these factors is more effective than either one alone (Powers & Shipe, 1928). Those fishes which can rapidly change the alkali reserve of their blood survive unfavorable gas conditions best. In worms also the rate of oxygen consumption decreases lineally as the oxygen in the medium decreases (Hall, 1931). The rate of oxygen consumption varies in invertebrates (Jordan, 1930; Duryee, 1932) and vertebrates (Hall, 1929) according to the amount of haemoglobin present in the blood. Mollusks and crustaceans pass more easily to land than vertebrates because the loading tension of haemocyanin is lower than that of haemoglobin in corpuscles. In solution (oligochaetes) haemoglobin has lower tension of loading than any other respiratory pigment (Carter, 1931). Among plethodontid salamanders "the most terrestrial species are least active and have the lowest rate of oxygen consumption (Evans, 1939). As the habitats of estuarine crabs "approached land there was an increase in oxygen consumption" (Ayers, 1938).

In many aquatic invertebrates the functioning of gills for respiration is essential for life. For example, if the circulation of water through the branchial chamber of a crab is prevented, death results (Hogben & Zoond, 1930). But there are some aquatic animals, such as may-fly nymphs and caddis-fly larvae, which can live for weeks or months after their gills have been removed (Morgan & O'Neil, 1931; Morgan & Grierson, 1932), though their respiration rate is slower. The land hermit crab *Coenobita clypeatus* Herbst lives for months without gills if kept in air, but dies more quickly in sea water without gills than with them (Borradaile, 1903; Pearse, 1932). The so-called blood gills of certain insects are not always respiratory in function. Those of mosquito and caddis-fly larvae (Morgan & O'Neil, 1931; Wigglesworth, 1933, a, b) appear to be water-absorbing organs.

Many animals that live in water must breathe air and will drown if continually submerged and prevented from reaching the surface. This is true of quite a number of species of fishes. Representatives of some of these are able to wander over land at intervals and in some cases to live for months or years out of water; others never leave the water, and die quickly if they do so. Das (1927), Henninger (1907), Hora (1933), and others have studied tropical air-breathing fishes which possess gills and special organs which are adapted for breathing air gulped in from the surface. These fishes die in from half an hour to four hours when immersed in water. On the other hand, many animals that possess lungs for air-breathing can live if those organs are removed. Krogh (1904) showed that a frog can respire enough through its skin to live after its lungs have been lost. Helff (1929, 1931) extirpated the lungs of frog tadpoles and found that "the young frogs lived for three to four weeks following complete metamorphosis." Yet he also demonstrated that the lungs of tadpoles were functional for a considerable period prior to metamorphosis. The axolotl (Ambystoma larva) survives after the removal of both lungs and gills, its skin being adequate for all its respiration (Hogben, 1926). Some amphibians are peculiarly adapted to live without the lungs, which were doubtless characteristic of ancestral amphibians. Some highly aquatic frogs have reduced lungs (Noble, 1925); salamanders of certain species have no lungs whatever, and their respiration is through enteric membranes and skin. In both these types of amphibians there is a tendency toward the reduction of the heart from a 3-chambered to a 2-chambered condition by the loss of the left auricle and the loss of the spiral valve. In salamanders with lungs (Ambystoma) the development of lungs precedes that of the auricular septum (Mekeel, 1930). Gage (1892) suggested that, in combining adaptations for respiration in water and air, animals often retained the former largely for excreting carbon dioxide and the latter for acquiring oxygen.

Aquatic animals in the past have become adapted many times to air-breathing, in or out of water. This has apparently happened most often in marshes and swamps where there was a lack of oxygen and along ocean beaches where tidal rhythms frequently left animals exposed. Fishes may have the swim-bladder adapted for breathing air. In gars (Lepisosteus), bowfins (Amiatus), and some other ganoids the swim-bladder serves as an important organ of respiration. Such fishes are able to live in stagnant water where oxygen is low by gulping air from the surface (Potter, 1927). In a genus (Nemachilus) of Indian loaches the swim-bladder varies in different species in accordance with the need of it for respiration. "In swift currents it is greatly reduced and enclosed in bone; in deep waters of lakes and at high altitudes it is re-developed" (Hora, 1930a). Morris (1892) believed that the swim-bladder of fishes was first developed for respiration and in teleosts secondarily took on hydrostatic functions. The gills of fishes, though often covered by opercula, are in a sense "open" organs of respiration, but swim-bladders, lungs, and other similar organs for air-breathing are in a sense "closed" as they enclose internal cavities (Powers *et al.*, 1932).

Fishes have become adapted to air-breathing in diverse and peculiar ways. Gobies which skip about on muddy ocean beaches have the adductors of the gill arches poorly developed; the epithelia of their gill filaments show more mucous, cornified, and albumen-secreting cells, and thus desiccation is inhibited; gill surfaces are reduced; the skin, buccal, and branchial epithelia may serve for respiration; in some species there is a cavity above the first gill; the mouth is small; the opercular aperture is narrow (Schöttle, 1931). Young land gobies have gills like aquatic gobies, but these change with other features during metamorphosis. In modern gobies and blennies "skin respiration is improved by the penetration of capillaries into the epidermis. An extreme saccular enlargement of the buccopharyngeal cavity increases the efficiency of buccal respiration. Gulped air is prevented from escaping through the gill slits by a modification of the gill covers" (Noble, 1931).

Bridge (1904) and Rauther (1910) have described the various types of air-breathing which occur in fishes. Their lists include the

Fig. 15. Beach-skipping gobies from Siam. These fish do not enter the water but skip about on mud beaches. They have vascular respiratory areas in and near their tails.

skin; air bladder; expansions from the buccopharyngeal cavity; labyrinthine organs contained in such cavities and mostly developed from gill arches; lung-like growths from the pharyngeal cavity; and vascular intestines aerated by bubbles taken in through the mouth. There has been no uniformity in the development of such organs in particular groups of fishes. They therefore appear to be of independent origin. For example, the silurid fishes show three or four different types of air-breathing organs. Carter & Beadle (1931) in their investigations in the tropical swamps of the Gran Chaco found four types of air-breathing organs in fishes: (1) lung-like air bladder, (2) large gill chamber without special structural adaptations, (3) vascular intestine with contained air bubbles, and (4) vascular stomach with contained air bubbles. They give a list of all air-breathing fishes in the world, with their types of adaptations.

Amphibians furnish an interesting series of types ranging from those which are aquatic in all stages in their life cycles (Siren, Necturus) to those which are completely terrestrial (Plethodon). Many begin their lives in water as tadpoles and metamorphose later into land animals. The American newt, *Triturus viridescens* Rafinesque, may remain aquatic throughout its life (Noble, 1929) or spend two or three years on land, and then return to the water to breed. "The subjection of the incompletely metamorphosed newts to terrestrial conditions causes a reduction of the gill stubs. . . . Siren is a form which has ceased to differentiate most of its structures beyond the stage characteristic of the early larva" (Noble, 1929). Morgan & Sondheim (1932) found that keeping gilled newts in a dry environment caused no reduction of gills, but the transplantation of portions of anterior pituitary lobe into the bodies of animals induced both males and females to become sexually mature though still bearing gills.

A frog tadpole is in a state somewhat comparable to an adult dipnoan. According to Willem (1920), a frog passes through five stages in regard to its respiration: (1) tadpole with internal gills like a fish, (2) tadpole with perforate nostrils and buccal respiratory movements, (3) young frog depending on cutaneous and buccopharyngeal respiration, (4) terrestrial young frog still dependent upon cutaneous and buccopharyngeal respiration, and (5) a frog dependent largely on lungs but still using skin when necessary. Certain salamanders that live in brooks and on land have no lungs and depend on buccopharyngeal and cutaneous breathing. The cutaneous respiration of a frog is not under the control of the nervous system, but pulmonary respiration is (Krogh, 1904). Certain African tadpoles (Hoplophryne), which live on bamboos and banana plants, hatch with functional lungs. They never develop external gills, and their internal gills are rudimentary (Noble, 1929a).

The changes in respiratory organs which have fitted animals to live on land have among fishes and amphibians been largely developed in connection with migrations from fresh water to land, but among crustaceans there are many examples of such modifications associated with migrations across ocean beaches, directly from sea to land. Littoral hermit crabs (Paguridea), arranged in order from deep-water to terrestrial types, show a progressive reduction in the number of gills (Fig. 16). Littoral crabs (Brachyura) in a similar fashion show a progressive reduction in gill volume in relation to

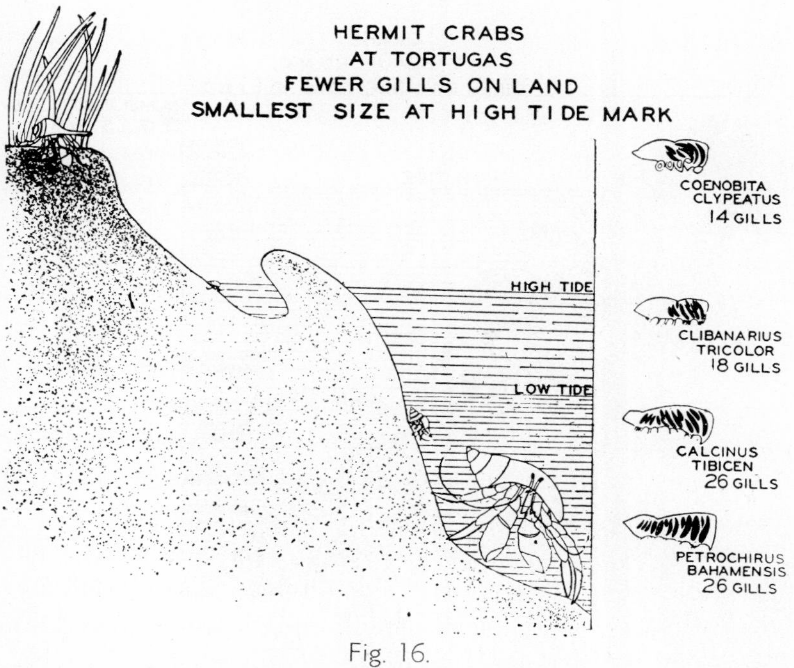

Fig. 16.

body volume (Fig. 17). At Tortugas and on the North Carolina coast a littoral aquatic crab has a body which is about twenty times the volume of the gills, but in a land crab the body has sixty times the volume of the gills (Pearse, 1929, 1929a). A land hermit crab will live several months after its gills have been removed (Borradaile, 1903; Pearse, 1929). An intertidal crab (Uca) may carry water in its branchial chamber. "The fiddler crab is a true water-

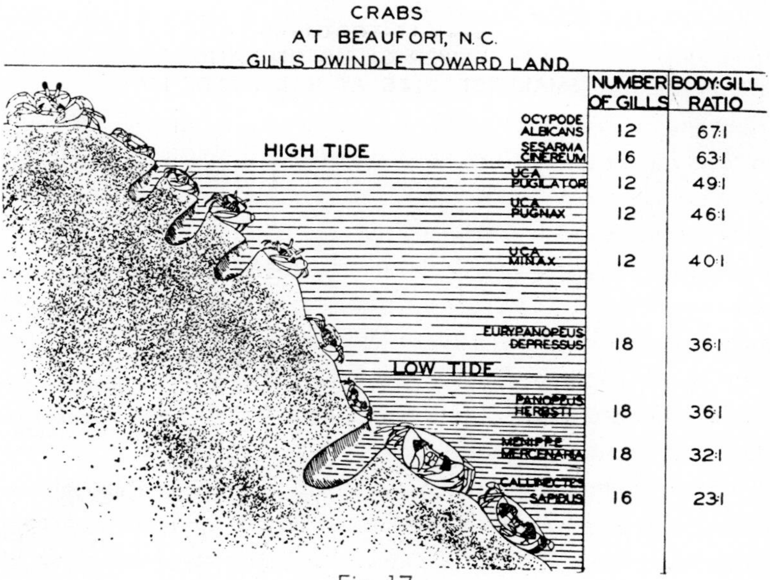

CRABS
AT BEAUFORT, N. C.
GILLS DWINDLE TOWARD LAND

HIGH TIDE

LOW TIDE

	NUMBER OF GILLS	BODY:GILL RATIO
OCYPODE ALBICANS	12	67:1
SESARMA CINEREUM	16	63:1
UCA PUGILATOR	12	49:1
UCA PUGNAX	12	46:1
UCA MINAX	12	40:1
EURYPANOPEUS DEPRESSUS	18	36:1
PANOPEUS HERBSTI	18	36:1
MENIPPE MERCENARIA	18	32:1
CALLINECTES SAPIDUS	16	23:1

Fig. 17.

breathing animal, but it can live in the air for several weeks without changing the water in the gill-chambers" (Dembowski, 1926). Barnacles, on the other hand, though bound to the ocean forever by their sessile mode of life and method of feeding, are terrestrial rather than aquatic animals in their respiration (Monterosso, 1927). Verwey (1930) has classified littoral crabs according to their methods of respiration as follows:

I. Water Crabs with Large Inhalent Opening: portunids such as Scylla, Neptunus, Thalamita.

II. Transition Breathers without Large Inhalent Opening:
   1. Pumpers: Pump water out of branchial chamber. Sesarma, Ilyoplax, Metaplax, Macrophthalmus.
   2. Non-pumpers: Circulate air through water in branchial chamber.
      a. Having normal course through branchial chamber. Grapsus, Potamon.
      b. Having special respiratory openings between 3rd and 4th legs. Uca, Ocypode.

There are land crabs (Gecarcinus, Cardisoma) which do not carry water in their gill chambers, and the respiratory cavities of Ocypode are not completely filled with water (Pearse, 1929).

As aquatic crabs take up life on land, various changes take place in their respiratory organs (von Raben, 1934). Often the gill cover takes on greater respiratory functions and in some cases becomes quite vascular, even developing lacunar systems which are surrounded by capillaries. The chitinous covering of the gills tends to become thicker. There are mechanisms for keeping the gill plates moist; in some cases water passes from the mouth through a special canal to the gills. Some land crabs breathe through vascular areas on the abdomen. And beach-skipping gobies breathe in part through their tails (Roughley, 1947).

Marine mollusks are for the most part gill-breathers, but a few littoral species have become air-breathers. River snails are commonly water-breathing, but in swamps and marshes air-breathing is the rule, and land snails are generally pulmonates.

Annelids which live in tubes or in stagnant water often develop gills, which are commonly evaginations of the skin. In the swamps of the Gran Chaco, Carter & Beadle (1931a) studied methods of respiration in eight species of oligochaetes. They do not believe that any of these worms can live anaerobically, but that all are able to endure low oxygen contents in the medium in which they live. One Aelosoma lived in the narrow oxygenated surface stratum, building a tube attached to plants. One large species (Drilocrius) burrowed in mud in shallow water. It was found to have a groove on its back in which it carried down a bubble from the surface.

There is abundant evidence from the past and present which indicates that air-breathing originated on beaches and in stagnant water long before life developed on land (Pearse, 1930, 1932b). Hall (1924) believes that primitive cartilaginous fishes (Chondrostei) used vascular enteric membranes for breathing from air that they had gulped in. One line of development (Holostei, Teleostei) from these emphasized the swim-bladder as a respiratory-hydrostatic organ, and another line (Crossopterygii, Dipnoi, Amphibia) developed a lung. Hall also points out that toads have improved their lung as an organ for use on land over that of aquatic salientians by enclosing the alveolar sacs more completely, so that they better conserve water. Reptiles have further isolated lobules by the development of branching bronchi. "The respiratory organs of terrestrial vertebrates are lungs. These arose in phylogeny long before the land was invaded" (Noble, 1931). "Aerial respiration was apparently first achieved by ganoid forms higher than the elasmobranchs, but ancestral to the Crossopterygii and Dipnoi. . . . A lung in the form of an air bladder opening off the ventral surface of the esophagus was present in the early ganoids before the line leading to the early Dipnoi, the Crossopterygii, and the Amphibia was separated from the parent stem" (Smith, 1931). A primitive type of lung persists today in the Dipnoi. "The breathing of atmospheric air had already been acquired by several groups of fishes of the ancient coal swamps, as it has by several unrelated modern fishes. If we may judge from modern conditions, an oxygen-secreting pouch long served to tide the fish over periods of drought, and possibly the stout fan-shaped paddles assisted them in wiggling from one pool to another. When breathing by the air-sac finally superseded breathing by gills, in the adult stage, it is not surprising that the opercular bones, which play an important part in branchial respiration, should have failed to ossify, leaving only a dermal flap. The region of the otic notch in Amphibia corresponds closely to the opercular flap in fishes" (Gregory, 1933). Morris (1892), Spengel (1904), Ballantyne (1927), Goodrich (1930), and others have discussed the origin of lungs.

Pike (1924) has reviewed the changes in vertebrate respiratory mechanisms. The appearance of lungs necessitated the development of new respiratory muscles. Coördination between swallowing and breathing was necessary. At first the body wall functioned for breathing. A reptile could live out of water. It might swallow in a leisurely way and breathe at the same time. A mammal with a diaphragm did even better. New nervous and muscular mechanisms made possible the methods of breathing which are now correlated with the rapid metabolism of homoiothermic animals.

Body Fluids

"The first living forms had the sea for their environment. Every cell, doubtless, came into contact with this fluid which was at the same time the source of its food and of its oxygen supply. As cells began to be associated in smaller or larger masses, channels were left between them through which the water of the sea might find passage. Animals a little farther along the scale of development shut off their body cavities, vascular and otherwise, from direct communication with the sea, but did not succeed in freeing the cells from the necessity of getting their food and oxygen supplies by diffusion from a solution. The fluid shut within the animal body furnished the immediate environment of the cells; it took the place of the sea in the economy of the organism. It has been seen that the fluid becomes more and more complex in structure as one passes in review from lower to higher forms. And while the internal fluid sea, bathing the individual cells, has become in some respects more complex and able to play a greater variety of functions in the life of the organisms, there are certain features in which it harks back to the primitive conditions which must have existed millions of years ago" (Rogers, 1927).

The salt systems which bathe the living cells of those animals in which body fluids differ from those in sea water do not have the same proportions of salts as occur in the ocean. Those in fresh-water animals of course differ markedly in salinity and composition from the surrounding medium. However, as Dakin (1912) has pointed out, an aquatic organism is not a closed system which is independent of changes in its environment. Such changes may affect internal media physically or chemically. The bloods of marine animals may differ markedly from those in the surrounding ocean. The salts in sipunculids and starfishes are about the same as those in the sea; but the quantity of those in crab and snail bloods are always at least a little below; and those in fishes are much less and rather constant (Duval, 1924, 1927). On the whole, the blood of many marine invertebrates is much like the ocean, but vertebrate blood substances always differ from the surrounding medium. "Marine invertebrates which have invaded brackish and fresh waters often present an independence of the blood which is not at all unlike that of vertebrates. For example, in both the fresh-water crayfish and a frog immersed in water, there is a constant controlled diffusion inwards of water and a regulated output from the excretory organs. A new fresh-water crab (from a river in New South Wales) with which we have been experimenting retains a constancy of blood salinity which is less than half that of the ocean from which it undoubtedly wandered, yet its sojourn in fresh water cannot have been of long duration" (Dakin, 1931).

The salt content of fresh water is not only less than that of the ocean but differs in composition. "In striking contrast to these [sea] solutions, in which sodium is 30 to 50 times more concentrated than the calcium, are the dilute salt systems in which avascular fresh-water animals are found. Two salient characteristics emerge from a review of a number of analyses of different fresh waters:

SALINITY OF CRAB BLOOD

The depression of the freezing point of blood (△) indicates the amount of salt present. Salinity decreases as crabs live away from sea.

Tortugas, Florida	°C		Misaki, Japan	°C
Gecarcinus lateralis	–1.65	Land ↑	Sesarma haematocheir	–1.43
Cardisoma guanhumi	–1.66		Sesarma pictum	–2.17
Ocypode albicans	–1.70		Hemigrapsus sanguineus	–2.19
Grapsus grapsus	–1.92		Pachygrapsus crassipes	–2.24
Mithrax verrucosus	–2.07	↓ Sea	Pugettia quadridens	–2.27
Coenobita clypeatus	–2.09	Land ↑		
Petrochirus bahamensis	–2.09			
Panulirus argus	–2.20	↓ Sea		
Sea Water	–2.04		Sea Water	–2.09

Fig. 18.

(1) they are much more dilute than the blood of higher forms, being about 0.01 per cent total salt; (2) the calcium is quite generally more concentrated than the sodium and the potassium together" (Hetherington, 1932). Marine animals which attempt to enter fresh water usually are not killed so much by dilution as by loss of essential salts (Sumner, 1906; Adolph, 1925; Hill, 1931). "If we consider any of the natural waters—lake, sea, spring, rain, or spring water—there will be found a general qualitative resemblance in the inorganic content. The fact that the internal medium of the higher animals has an inorganic composition *qualitatively* similar to that of the natural waters is scarcely surprising. What is physiologically important is the *quantitative* pattern" (Conway, 1945). A conger eel may survive for days in 0.1 sea water but dies in a few hours in fresh water (Hill, 1931).

Sea waters and bloods are complex systems which contain salts, organic materials, colloids, ions, and other substances which may affect organisms. Each substance probably has more or less specific effects on protoplasm and vital processes. Some marine animals contain more than 99% water in their bodies (Gortner, 1933). Others commonly maintain body fluids which contain such mixtures of salts and organic materials as to make them slightly denser than the sea water. Other marine animals maintain their body fluids in a steady state which is much less dense than sea water. Three types of equilibria occur in animals, and these represent different osmotic relations with the environment: (1) body fluids are isotonic and isohalin with the external medium; (2) body fluids are isotonic but not isohalin with the external medium; and (3) the body fluids differ in osmotic pressure and content from the external medium, and are therefore more or less independent of environment (Fredericq, 1922). Representatives of all these types live in the ocean today. In animals osmotic pressure cannot rise much above that of the environment (Shelford, 1929), but in plants it may be two or three times as great (Atkins, 1917). It has been suggested by some that the low and more or less stable osmotic pressures that are characteristic of vertebrate blood are survivals of conditions in primitive seas which had an osmotic pressure of perhaps a third what it is today (Wardlaw, 1931); but such arguments are made questionable by the fact that bony fishes appear to have had their origin in fresh water (Barrell, 1916; Case, 1919), though the remoter ancestors of fishes were probably marine. Blood is not derived from the waters of old oceans but from the body fluids of the the inhabitants of those oceans (Dakin, 1912).

As animals left the ocean to invade fresh-water and land habitats, there were changes in the character of limiting membranes and the body fluids. In animals there are two lines of defense, so to speak, where changes may be permitted, controlled, or prevented: the membranes on the outsides of bodies and those covering cells which may lie deep in the interior. In protozoans and sponges there is little distinction between these, but in metazoans which have inclosed blood and lymph systems the distinction is marked. In aquatic animals the permeability of the external membranes is of primary importance. Many marine animals permit all constituents of sea water to pass in and out of their bodies. Changes in the osmotic pressure of external media in general limit the distribution of fresh-water animals more than those of marine animals. In gaining ability to retain salts in hypotonic media, the latter have apparently lost ability to adjust to changes (Adolph, 1925).

A frog tadpole at the time of its metamorphosis undergoes marked changes in regard to the ability of its skin to resist changes in the osmotic pressure of the surrounding medium (Adolph, 1925, 1927a, b). An adult frog apparently has a mechanism in its skin which is under nervous control and which regulates somewhat the passage of water and solutes (Adolph, 1933). There is general agreement that animals which have gained ability to regulate or resist diffusion processes through their external membranes have done so by the addition of controlling mechanisms. An animal that maintains a dynamic steady state during which its internal fluids differ in osmotic pressure and composition from those outside must continually do work (Adolph, 1925; Pantin, 1931; Hill, 1931); the regulation is not merely diffusion but an active process carried on by living tissues.

Schlieper (1930) classifies animals as homoiosmotic, in which the body fluids differ from the surrounding medium, and poikilosmotic, in which they are essentially the same. Oxygen requirements and O_2 consumption increase in euryhaline invertebrates as the salt concentration of the external medium decreases. "It is assumed that this increased respiration is required for the work done against an osmotic intake of water from the outside." In Australia Edmonds (1935) tested species of crabs from diverse habitats. "Five species . . . have been found to be homoiosmotic in diluted sea water." One species was poikilosmotic. Black (1948) studied the adjustment of Fundulus to fresh water and found that it involved changes in gas in the swim-bladder, chloride content of body fluids, weight, and density. The gain in weight was temporary, due to water absorption. After 10 days in fresh water 10% of Cl was lost. In fresh water the fish sank and regained buoyancy by secreting gases into the swim-bladder. All these changes took place in 24 hours, but when a fish was replaced in sea water it regained its normal density in 6 hours.

Beadle (1934) has studied a flatworm (*Gunda ulvae*) which lives where it is alternately subjected to water from streams and from the ocean. This worm can live permanently in any concentration of sea water down to 5%. It is able to maintain a relatively constant internal state against a rapidly changing external environment. When it is transferred to dilute sea water there is an initial flow of water through the integument into the parenchyma, which causes swelling and a temporary lowering of activity. The water is soon taken up by the gut, and forms intracellular vacuoles. This process requires an expenditure of energy, as it is inhibited by cyanide. The parenchyma soon returns to its original condition and resumes its normal activity. Then the animal sets up a resistance, and the integument becomes less permeable, but the gut remains vacuolated as long as it is in dilute water. The excretory system does not appear to be concerned particularly with such regulatory processes. "Distinction must be drawn between the ultimate impermeability of the ectoderm considered as a membrane and the osmotic resistance of the individual cells of this layer and of other tissues. The permeability of the ectodermal membrane can be reversibly increased by calcium deficiency, but the osmotic resistance of its individual cells cannot be broken down by this means." Both the vacuole formation by the gut and the osmotic resistance developed by individual cells are believed to be active processes which expend energy, but the impermeability of the external membrane is a passive process.

The salinity of body fluids of animals is influenced chiefly by three factors: (1) external membranes, (2) products of metabolism present in the internal medium, and (3) renal organs (Dakin, 1912). In fresh water the blood of crustaceans generally has a higher salinity than that of mollusks. Such differences are inherent and dependent on characteristic racial adaptations. In the ocean the salt content of the bloods of sharks and bony fishes is similar. But the blood of a shark is isotonic with sea water, its osmotic pressure being maintained by the presence of large quantities of urea, while that of a teleost has only about a third of the osmotic pressure of sea water. European littoral crabs present a graded series in regard to their ability to maintain a constant internal medium: the blood of Hyas rapidly becomes isotonic with sea water or dilutions of it which surround its body; Cancer changes much more slowly; and Carcinus is little influenced by changes in the salinity of the water around it. When placed in diluted sea water Hyas absorbs water and increases in weight rapidly; Cancer changes more slowly, and some individuals change very little; Carcinus does not change

(Schlieper, 1929, 1933). Crustaceans, in order to attain equilibrium with the surrounding medium in dilute solutions, excrete water largely through the kidneys (Schlieper, 1933), but fishes lose water chiefly through their gills and other external membranes (Dakin, 1912).

A fresh-water clam has little ability to resist osmotic changes in hypertonic solutions, and dies rather quickly in salt water (Fig. 19), but a crayfish is more hardy. The former has little salt and little organic matter in its blood; the latter has much of both. A crayfish

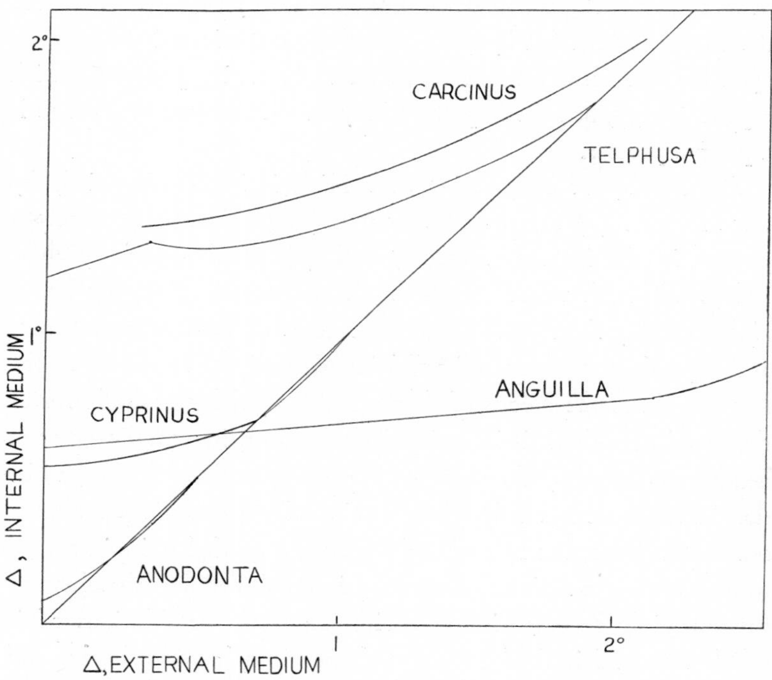

Fig. 19. The relation between molecular concentration of the blood and that of the external medium in various aquatic animals: Anodonta sp., Carcinus maenas, Telphusa fluviatile, Anguilla, and Cyprinus carpio. (After Schlieper, 1933.)

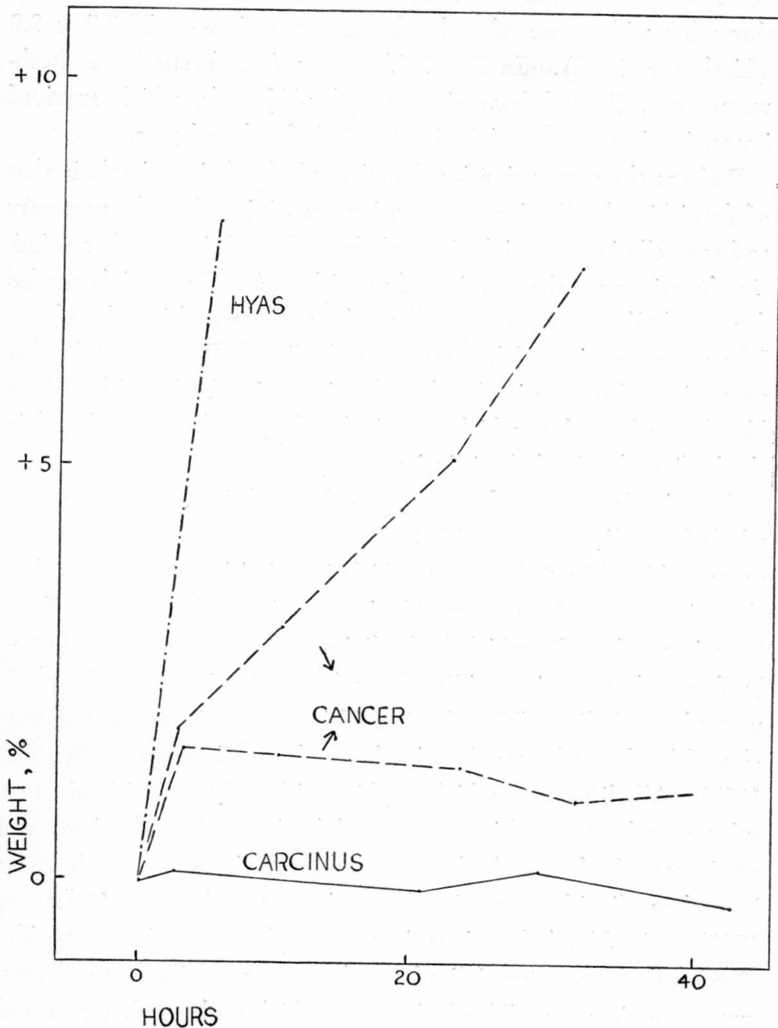

Fig 20. Changes in weight of Hyas aranea, Cancer pagurus, and Carcinus meanas after transfer from the North Sea (salinity, 3.2%) to brackish water (salinity, 2%). (After Schlieper, 1933.)

heart when perfused with various solutions continues to beat through a wide range of molecular concentrations,—pH 5.5 to 9.0 (Lindeman, 1928). In Siam, Alexander (1932) studied a fresh-water crab, *Paratelphusa sinense* Milne-Edwards, which survived immersion in sea water (pH 3.0 to 10.0) for four hours.

Perhaps the most primitive function of bloods in animals is that of furnishing bodily tissues a solution containing the salts necessary to keep cells in a physiologically balanced condition. Other primitive functions are the carrying of nourishment and materials needed for metabolic processes, as well as the wastes resulting therefrom. The transportation of hormones, antibodies, leucocytes, and other protective substances is also done by circulating body fluids. Many bloods produce clots which effectively plug up holes produced in the bodies of animals by injuries.

As animals progress from ocean to land, their bloods are on the whole less saline (Pearse, 1931, 1932b; Rogers, 1927, p. 148) and more stable (Fig. 18). Salts, which in primitive animals are like those in the sea, become specific in quantity and function. They keep internal media which bathe living cells constant by acting as buffers and preventing acidity through combinations with the products of metabolism. More lactic acid is secreted in the active muscles of land vertebrates than in those of aquatic animals (Ritchie, 1927). Alkali reserves which combine with carbon dioxide or other substances become subject to control by internal mechanisms and are increased when such changes as decrease in oxygen or increase in carbon dioxide occur in the environment (Powers & Logan, 1925). As blood functions increase and become more specific, blood cells become specialized as phagocytes, antibody producers, oxygen carriers, etc. Blood pigments, which perhaps first occurred as inert waste products, came to serve important functions as oxygen carriers. They may be present in the plasma or confined to particular cells or corpuscles. Haemoglobin occurs in vertebrates in corpuscles, except in the lancelets in which it is plasmic. It is also found in various crustaceans, insects, mollusks, annelids, gephyreans, echinoderms, and nemerteans. Haemocyanin, which contains copper, is found in various crustaceans, arachnids, gastropods, and cephalopods. Other respiratory pigments are found as follows: chlorocruorin, chaetopods; haemerythrin, gephyreans; chlorophyl, lepidopterous insects; and tetronerythrin, decapod crustaceans.

Fig. 21. A fresh water crab from Colombia.

The occurrence of respiratory pigments is without reference to phylogenetic relationship. Some chironomid larvae which live in stagnant water contain so much haemoglobin that they have long been known as blood worms; others which dwell in well-aerated waters are quite transparent. It has been said that haemoglobin occurs where there is a dearth of oxygen,—often in aquatic habitats on account of a deficiency in the environment, and often in aquatic and terrestrial habitats where an impervious external covering of a large body make the carrying of sufficient oxygen to internal tissues difficult.

Body fluids changed, as animals were gradually transformed from marine to fresh water and land animals, from actual sea water to comparatively dilute, exactly regulated, viscous, nutritious, corpusculated, and pigmented liquids. Instead of furnishing merely suitable media for bathing living cells, they have come to serve a variety of functions concerned with nutrition, respiration, excretion, the humoral control of activities, and the prevention of damage from disease or injury. The history of the rise of land animals has been a bloody one. Emphasis has shifted from dependence on a primitive dependable external medium to that on a specialized, highly regulated, internal medium.

Metabolism

The quality of metabolism in all animals is apparently similar, but the rate varies markedly on account of inherent hereditary qualities and because of variations in environment. Size has a marked influence on rate of metabolism on account of surface-mass relations. A man to keep his body warm must expend food equal to about 1% of his body weight each day; a mouse, 25%; and an insect, if it were to maintain the same temperature as a mammal, 625% (Kennedy, 1927a). It is apparent that an insect must continue to be poikilothermic, and can be active therefore only when its environment is warm. Animals consume about the same amount of total energy per gram during their lives (Rubner, 1924b). Smaller animals live faster, shorter lives than larger animals. Rats live twice as long if prevented from exercising as when they exercise, because they expend energy more slowly (Slonaker, 1926). The longevity of many poikilothermic animals is more or less directly related to rate of metabolism, as determined by temperature (MacArthur & Baillie, 1929).

The most active marine fishes have most haemoglobin in their blood and carry on metabolism at a high rate; sluggish fishes are better able to utilize oxygen when it occurs in low concentrations, and to endure lack of oxygen (Hall, 1929). Rate of metabolism has apparently not been an important factor in the migration of fishes from sea to fresh water or land, but it has been for many invertebrates. For example, the respiratory rate of crabs varies more or less with the salt concentration in the surrounding medium. This happens because the rate of metabolism depends somewhat on the amount of osmoregulation required (Schwabe, 1933). Many marine invertebrates cannot increase their energy utilization in fresh water and therefore perish. Some, however, are able to make temporary or permanent adjustments to waters of low salt concentration. The kidneys of shrimp of the genus Palaemonetes and of other crustaceans vary in structure according to the salinity of the medium in which the animals live. The thyroid gland of vertebrates produces a hormone, thyroxin, which increases metabolic rate. "It seems the business of the gland to maintain in the blood a certain definite though small concentration of an iodine compound. In doing so it may, as has been suggested, maintain in the blood for the use of the body the iodine content of the sea, and may thus have made possible the evolution of the land animal" (Rogers, 1927). The temperature of a poikilothermic animal in any environment is as a rule a little higher than that of its surroundings. Such animals may raise their body temperatures a little by increasing their metabolism. Smith (1930) estimates that 15% of the metabolism of an active Protopterus is expended in muscular movements. On the whole, poikilothermic animals are at a disadvantage because many of their activities must be suspended when temperatures fall. When they leave aquatic habitats, where the high specific heat of water makes rapid change in temperature infrequent, they are often confined to situations where the environment prevents rapid changes. The soil, leafy ground litter, rotting logs, and similar refuges are commonly sought during cold or dry periods by primitive terrestrial animals.

Homoiothermism is perhaps the most important adaptation that animals have made to terrestrial life. By developing for living cells a favorable internal environment which remains quite constant chemically and thermally, animals have thus become more or less independent of environment (Pike & Scott, 1915; Pearse & Hall, 1928). The continual, rapid metabolism of homoiothermic animals has the disadvantage that large quantities of food must be available. The development of nutritious land plants was associated with and to some extent conditioned the development of homoiothermic land animals (Berry, 1920). A mouse at the same environmental temperature produces twenty-five times as much heat per day as a fish of the same size (Rubner, 1924). A poikilothermic animal may live for years without food, but a homoiothermic animal dies of starvation in a few months.

Benedict (1932) has made an extensive study of the differences between poikilothermic and homoiothermic animals. He finds that the temperature of the latter is higher than that of the former at any environmental temperature. A poikilothermic vertebrate warmed to 37° C. produces only one-third to one-eighth as much heat as a homoiothermic vertebrate. Benedict, after examining various possibilities, concludes that differences between the two are not due to differences in protoplasm, chemical constitution, or metabolism, though poikilothermic animals do contain more water and ash, less dry matter and active protoplasmic tissue than homoiothermic animals. The heart rate is higher and there is more blood in homoiothermic animals. "It is therefore believed that the *distribution of the blood* in the tissues may explain the difference in the metabolism of these animals. . . . Where there is a liberal supply of blood to the tissues heat production *can* be high. Where the blood supply is low, it *must* be low. . . . All these considerations lead to the conclusion that the distribution of the blood is the dominant factor in metabolism and that the higher metabolism of warm-blooded animals may be explained by the fact that in their case there is better distribution of blood to the outer tissues and peripheries." In mammals blood corpuscles are smaller than in fishes and amphibians. This increases relative surface and oxygen-carrying capacity.

Locomotion

There is no essential difference between the locomotor organs of marine and fresh-water animals, but those of animals which have left aquatic habitats to take up life on land have often been obliged to undergo considerable modification. In transferring its activities from water to land an animal enters a rarer medium and thus has an opportuntiy to move with a greater speed, but it cannot do this if it does not have sturdy locomotor organs which are able to support its body against the greater pull of gravity which results when the buoyancy of water is lost. Seals and whales are powerful and agile swimmers, but on land are awkward or incapable of locomotion.

The chief invaders of the land are: (1) animals which creep on slimy muscular surfaces, such as flatworms and snails; (2) those with hard exoskeletons, the arthropods; (3) and those with endoskeletons, the vertebrates. Terrestrial worms and mollusks have remained subterranean or are confined largely to moist situations. None has attained speed, which Jehu (1923) maintains is a primary quality of a typically terrestrial animal. It is the arthropods and tetrapod vertebrates which are today the dominant land animals.

Arthropods in any habitat are covered with a chitinous exoskeleton, which is also often impregnated with mineral salts and thus strengthened. Their jointed legs are suited for locomotion of various types. They may be flattened and provided with long bristles, and thus serve as admirable organs for swimming, or they may be provided with stout spines which hold fast when an animal runs on land. Arthropods appear to be related to annelids. In fact, if some polychaete annelids were to be provided with an exoskeleton, they would become arthropods without further modification. Harms (1929) has described a tough-skinned polychaete which walks about on land by using its parapodia somewhat as a centipede uses its legs. Land crustaceans have stouter, more spiny, and less setose limbs than their aquatic relatives; but a strictly aquatic crab which is suddenly placed on land is not unsuited to locomotion and, if permitted, quickly makes its way back to water. Crabs show various adaptations in foot structure for digging, clinging, etc. (Crane, 1947). The locomotor difficulties of arthropods in attaining land life have been few and simple.

The origin of the tetrapod limbs of vertebrates is more or less of a mystery, but paleontologists and comparative anatomists rather generally agree that they came from lobe-fins such as crossopterygian ganoids possessed in Devonian times. "The tendency toward the evolution of freely turning paddles, presumably out of fin-folds, reaches a climax among the lobe-finned fishes of late Paleozoic times . . . the paddles spread out like the sticks of a fan, and the bony rods that support them seem destined to give rise to the skeleton of the arm and hand in higher vertebrates" (Gregory, 1933). "At all events it is clear that we should expect the fish-like ancestors of the Tetrapoda to have possessed pectoral and pelvic fins alike in structure, with outstanding muscular lobe, extensive endoskeleton with at least five radials, small web, and few if any dermal rays" (Goodrich, 1930). Lull (1929) believes that the earliest tetrapod limbs may have been two-toed but agrees with others that the majority of primitive land vertebrates were five-toed.

The limbs of certain modern fishes which live out of water on muddy beaches have been described in considerable detail (Hamburger, 1904; Eggert, 1929a). The ventral, or posterior, fins of gobies often together form sucker-like organs which are used for locomotion on land and even for climbing. In land gobies there is a tendency to have a broad cleithrum at the base of the fin, the basal bones often fuse; fin rays are short and few; and special muscles develop for walking which are not present or are poorly developed in aquatic gobies. Changes from aquatic to land life involve better muscular development and nervous coördination (Pike, 1924).

Nervous System

As animals have progressed from aquatic to land life, they have attained greater speed in their locomotor responses to stimuli; more dependence has been placed on sense organs which give distant, rather than contact, perception; and more effective mechanisms have been developed for the control of bodily activities. Hormones, which in primitive metazoans are probably produced more or less by cells throughout the body of an animal, come to be secreted by definitely localized organs and are integrated with nervous mechanisms for the control of bodily functions.

In the ocean, where small organisms suitable for food float everywhere in the water and accumulate as oozes on the bottom, radial symmetry, with its decentralizing influences on nervous organization, is common. But on land there are no radially symmetrical animals. Terrestrial bilateral types show progressive cephalization and delegation of bodily control to nervous mechanisms, which perhaps have reached their climax in arboreal and aerial animals.

The eyes of terrestrial arthropods are often very large compared to those of types that live in water (Harms, 1929) and come to constitute a considerable portion of the nervous system (Kennedy, 1927a). The ghost crab, Ocypode, can see objects clearly at distances of 10 to 15 meters (Harms, 1929). The compound eye of an agile insect predator, such as a dragon-fly or a robber-fly, are very acute and may be made up of thousands of simple eyes. Stridulating organs are rare among aquatic arthropods, but the songs of land types are well known. Organs of hearing are proportionally well developed. Sensory hairs and gustatory and olfactory organs change their character completely when arthropods change their habitat from water to land (Marcus, 1911; Harms, 1929). Odors are important in the daily life of many land crustaceans (Borradaile, 1903; Harms, 1929) and constitute the basis for the social life of insects (Kennedy, 1927a). Some polychaete worms which live on land have sense organs which resemble those of arthropods (Harms, 1929).

The eyes of fishes which live on land have been much studied (Beer, 1894; Baumeister, 1913; Hess, 1913; Harms, 1914, 1929; Weve, 1922; Karsten, 1923; Schreitmuller & Relinghaus, 1926). The climbing perch (Anabas) has eyes like aquatic fishes, and is myopic in water and on land. The beach-skipping gobies belonging to the genus Periophthalmus, however, differ from other fishes in being hypermetropic and in other respects are adapted for life on land. In common with other fishes which live in mud these gobies have a liquid-filled chamber in front of the cornea for protection. They are unlike other fishes in having to accommodate their eyes for near vision, in having the eyes protuberant and quite movable, and in possessing a considerable degree of binocular vision. A beach-skipper can see a termite clearly at a distance of two to three meters.

Amphibia furnish favorable material for the study of changes in sense organs with the assumption of terrestrial life, because many of them spend part of their life on land and part in water. Matthes (1927) has investigated the olfactory organs of the European newt (Triturus). He finds that when a newt is changed from water to land there is a temporary loss of ability to smell, but recovery takes place after three or four days. The nasal epithelia are quite different in land and water newts. The olfactory hairs in the former are five times as long as those in the latter. If a terrestrial newt is replaced in water, its olfactory hairs soon shorten.

Excretion

"All organisms which have the power of regulating the osmotic pressure of their body fluids are provided with an excretory organ corresponding to a kidney" (Wardlaw, 1931). Probably the primitive function of renal organs was to regulate the osmotic pressure of internal fluids, and only secondarily have they assumed the elimination of metabolic wastes. All animals which live in fresh water, where the external medium is hypotonic to their body fluids, readily permit the return of water from their bodies to the outside. A Paramecium in 24 hours may eliminate water equal to 31 to 700 times its own volume, depending on temperature (Hesse, 1920).

The water-eliminating activities of kidneys are as a rule greater in fresh water than in the sea or on land because animals there live in solutions that are hypotonic to their body fluids. Crabs usually do not eliminate water through their kidneys, but crayfishes, fresh-water fishes, and amphibians do. Most marine crustaceans have urine which is isotonic with sea water, but fresh-water amphipods have larger kidneys than those that live in the ocean and excrete more water through them (Schlieper, 1933). The green gland of the land hermit crab Coenobita is reduced and lacks a terminal vesicle, thus differing from comparable marine crustaceans (Borradaile, 1903). "The glomerular development of the kidneys of vertebrates is related to water excretion. The protovertebrate kidney was at one stage probably aglomerular, and the glomerulus was evolved as an adaptation to a fresh-water habitat. In the lower vertebrates remaining in fresh water (dipnoans, ganoids, and fresh-water teleosts), and those still in intimate dependence on it (Amphibia), the glomerular development is good; but with the secondary assumption of marine habitat (marine teleosts) or with the assumption of terrestrial life in which water-conservation becomes a necessity (arid-living reptiles and birds) the glomerular development is poor" (Marshall & Smith, 1930; Baldwin, 1937). Mammals have modified the glomerulus into a filtration-reabsorption apparatus. Cyclostomes and elasmobranchs are like fresh-water fishes in glomerular development. Fishes transferred from sea water which is hypotonic to their body fluids to that which is hypertonic may, if they live, excrete salts through their kidneys (Schlieper, 1933; Smith, 1933). Frogs in water at 20°C. excrete water at the rate of 1.3% of their body weight per hour (Adolph, 1927a). Their urine is always hypotonic to their body fluids. But if the skin is dried or if the body is in hypertonic solutions a frog may absorb water from the bladder into the tissues (Steen, 1929). A man excretes a fiftieth of his body weight per day through his kidneys; a frog at ordinary temperatures, about a third.

Kidneys in all animals may perform two functions: (1) the regulation of the concentration of body fluids by conserving or eliminating water and solutes and (2) the excretion of the waste products of metabolism. Elasmobranchs retain urea in their blood to increase osmotic pressure (Scott, 1916; Denis, 1922); estivating lung-fishes may retain large quantities of urea in their bodies because the water needed for its excretion is not available (Smith, 1931). Many birds and desert reptiles excrete uric acid instead of urea; they thus conserve water, for the uric acid is practically insoluble. The evolution of the forms taken by nitrogenous wastes in various invertebrates (Delaunay, 1924) and vertebrates (Przylecki, 1926) is interesting but not particularly significant in connection with aboceanic migrations except for the fact that changes have been related to environmental conditions.

Reproduction

The eggs of some animals require salt in the surrounding medium for their development. "This dependence of the egg on the inorganic material of its environment . . . seems to be a significant limiting factor, making it impossible for marine animals to colonize fresh water, until, by some chance mutation, perhaps, the capacity for providing enough ash within the egg is acquired. To the factors defined by Sollas and von Martens we must add the importance of the fresh-water egg being supplied with materials that its inorganic surroundings cannot be expected to give it" (Needham, 1930). "The ova of Nereis are capable of fertilization and development in thirty-three and one-third per cent sea water" (Just, 1930, 1930a), but those of Echinarachnius and other marine animals die in rather slight dilutions. An eel, after a prolonged sojourn in fresh water, is prepared to reenter the ocean and lay its eggs by the increase of osmotic pressure in its body fluids, and this apparently occurs without any stimulating change in its surroundings (Johnstone, 1908). Gastrotricha show an interesting reaction to salinity. In the ocean they produce an abundance of males and zygotes, but in fresh water reproduction is parthenogenetic (Remane, 1929).

As some animals are limited to life in the ocean by salinity requirements, so some are kept in aquatic habitats by inability to carry on reproductive activities in the absence of water. The eggs of most fishes and amphibians are laid in water, but a few deposit them in air so that hatching young fall into the water. The spotted salamander, *Ambystoma maculatum* (Shaw), lays its eggs in ponds, but spends most of its adult life on land. Blanchard (1930) has studied the breeding habits of this species. "Migration to the breeding ponds depends on rain and not on temperature . . . in southern Michigan the spotted salamanders begin migration to the breeding ponds during the first rain at night following the disappearance of snow and thawing of the surface of the ground in the woods; . . . a prolonged rain, or several rains, will be required to bring all adult individuals of the species to the breeding sites." The marbled salamander, *Ambystoma opacum* (Gravenhorst), drowns in water. Its eggs are enclosed in four capsules and hence are fitted to some degree for life on land. They are usually deposited in situations where hatching tadpoles will be washed into water by rains;

but will hatch on land as well as in water (Noble & Brady, 1933). They will not hatch without considerable moisture, and tadpoles usually emerge during rains. Salamanders of the genus Plethodon have left the water during all stages in their life cycle. Their eggs are to be found in moist situations under logs and stones or in holes in the ground. The tadpole stage is passed within the egg membranes before hatching.

In Brazil, Lutz (1948) studied the life histories of frogs. She found that the "general trend is toward withdrawal of development from water, with concomitant changes in reproductive behavior, ecotopic adaptations, progressive increase of yolk volume and acceleration of development."

The chief reproductive adaptations which have enabled animals to leave the ocean and take up life in fresh water and on land are as follows: (1) Internal fertilization, which permits the union of gametes without reference to the character of the external medium. The union of gametes of many species takes place readily in fresh water but is of course impossible in air. Many male animals in marine, fresh-water, and land habitats produce spermatophores which are left to be picked up by, or actually injected into, females of the same species. (2) A shell, which protects and insulates—conserves water and salts; protects from desiccation and injury. (3) Food provision—as yolk in the egg cell, within the body of a parent through such structures as placentae, or even by the feeding of young, as by bees and birds. (4) Reduction in the number of young and better care of them by such membranes as those about eggs and the amnia of insects, birds, and mammals; by watchfulness and care by parents of eggs or young. Care may extend even to the keeping of the young warm by placing them in favorable situations or by heat from the parent's body and to education for the work of adult life. (5) Reduction of free-swimming larval stages and a general tendency toward vivaparousness. Fresh water has less buoyancy and free-swimming larval stages might be swept out to sea. There is little salt in fresh water and salts must be provided in the egg (Baldwin, 1937). (6) Adoption of peculiar breeding habits to avoid interspecific competition. The grunion deposits eggs in sand above the water, and other smelts leave their eggs in the sea. The species of

Fig. 22. A male fiddler crab waving at a female. On land sight and hearing are emphasized more than taste and smell in courtship.

shrimps in Chesapeake Bay breed at different seasons (Cowles, 1908). "The terrestrial stage in the life of *Ambystoma opacum* is an adaptation permitting the species to compete successfully in the same region with other species of *Ambystoma*" (Noble & Brady, 1933). Of course no single quality of those enumerated is absolutely characteristic of land or fresh water, but they indicate trends. There are marine elasmobranchs which nourish their young with secretions from the mother's uterus (Alcock, 1902).

In life cycles animals may show nicely graded series of stages connecting specialized with primitive conditions, or individuals, races, or species may be sharply segregated from others. Land crustaceans, which came originally from the sea, either produce marine free-swimming larvae from their eggs (Coenobita, Birgus, Uca, Cardisoma, Gecarcinus) or they do not (crayfishes; river crabs, Potamon). There are no intergrades. The littoral isopod *Ligia baudiniana* (Milne-Edwards) commonly avoids sea water and, when wetting its gills, carefully keeps its body from contact with it, but does not free its young from its brood-pouch unless submerged. The British littoral snails of the genus Littorina furnish a nice series of variations in breeding habits: *L. littorea* (L.), lowest on the beach, produces eggs which hatch out early veliger larvae; *L. obtusata* (L.) in the mid-tidal zone lays eggs which hatch out second-stage veligers; *L. saxatilis* (Oliv.) and *L. neritoides* L. are viviparous and thus best adapted to the dryer conditions near high-tide mark (Colgan, 1910; Flattely & Walton, 1922).

Some animals in their life cycles reproduce events which represent critical transformations that their ancestors struggled to attain in the past. A tadpole when it metamorphoses into a frog changes and improves its powers of regulating osmotic pressures within its body, and the acquirement of this new ability is simultaneous with the cessation of the use of the gills (Adolph, 1927b). A few fishes "undergo a certain metamorphosis into partly terrestrial animals, and Harms found that this metamorphosis was influenced by the thyroid hormone, as in the case of Amphibia" (Noble, 1931). The land hermit crab *Birgus latro* Leach, when young, inserts its twisted abdomen in a snail's shell, like other hermit crabs. As it grows larger, it finally is unable to find a shell big enough for its abdomen, which then becomes bilaterally symmetrical and bears hard chitinous plates on its dorsum (Harms, 1932).

The development of an animal requires a certain environment, which in many cases is the sea or is a sea-like liquid enclosed within an egg shell. Energy is also necessary, and, as a rule, much of this is supplied from food stored in the egg itself, but at times it is supplied from other sources, such as secretions from a parent, or other foods. A variable environment, if it is not too dry or too cold, tends to hasten development (Shelford, 1929). Land habitats, because they vary more, in general are populated by animals which show well-marked seasonal rhythms and often have very brief developmental periods unless the young are retained within the body of the parent or live in some special terrestrial habitat where conditions of life are constant. For example, the tadpoles of highly terrestrial amphibians have shorter lives than those which are more aquatic. A spade-foot toad tadpole transforms into an adult in two to four weeks after hatching, but a bullfrog tadpole lives for a year or two (Wright, 1931).

Reproductive and growth processes are more or less rhythmic and are usually orderly and cyclic (Flattely, 1920; Brody, 1928; Adolph, 1931a). In stable, uniform environments, such as the open ocean furnishes, animals are often erratic and perennial, but in the littoral marine region, in fresh water, and on land they are usually definitely correlated with seasonal successons. Hubbs (1928) believes that in fishes "structural differences between local races seem largely the result of changes in developmental rate (and metabolism), not themselves of direct selectional significance. A harmonious relation exists between the developmental rate and the usual environmental conditions during growth. Normal development is possible with some variation in conditions. But when a new territory is populated, with, for instance, a lower temperature, the individuals are brought closer to the threshold of abnormal development, and a higher rate of elimination must result. A mutation covering the developmental metabolism would adjust the population to the new habitat. Such changes as an increase in segments would secondarily result. The population would increase and push on into still colder waters, where the same modifications would be expected. A series of such primary physiological and secondarily structural alterations would produce the graded series of local races often exhibited in the latitudinal variation of fishes."

Food

As has been pointed out (p. 91), animals that live in water are surrounded by food in the form of small plants and animals and as dissolved substances. In the ocean algae of some size and a few higher plants are present along shore, but these constitute a very small part of available food resources. In fresh water a considerable body of submerged and emergent vascular vegetation is available. On land the bulk of the plant food of animals is made up of spermatophytes. Pütter's idea (1909) that aquatic animals absorb considerable amounts of organic food through external bodily membranes seems to have been pretty will disproved (Dakin, 1925; Krogh, 1931), but some aquatic animals undoubtedly do utilize such nourishment as colloidal material which is taken from water passed through the enteron (Hinman, 1932; Smith, 1933).

In any habitat animals tend to be specialists in their food relations, although there are always omnivorous animals of both specialized and generalized types. Animals commonly avoid competition by using different foods (Pearse, 1930, 1934). Along the shores of aquatic habitats the majority of animals are vegetarians, mud eaters, and scavengers (Pearse, 1929, 1932a). Carnivores must always occur in smaller numbers than the animals upon which they prey. Animals which have attained terrestrial life have been obliged to restrict their digestive activities to the interior of their bodies. Organs of taste, instead of being scattered over the outside surfaces, are limited to the region about the mouth (insects) or to the buccal cavity itself (land vertebrates). In finding foods, more dependence is usually placed on organs (olfactory, visual, auditory) which receive stimuli from a distance. Glands along the digestive canal are more sharply defined. Water is added to food by salivary glands near the anterior end of the alimentary canal and removed from it near the posterior end. A snail's radula, which is an old organ developed in the ocean, is an admirable mechanism for rasping off bits of land plants for foods. A carp has no stomach and no peptic digestion (Kenyon, 1925); there is much enteric variation among fishes according to food habits. Among mammals there are many differences in food habits, but there is comparatively slight variation in organs of digestion. There is no mammal without a stomach. A primary distinction between reptiles, as terrestrial types, and amphibians, as aquatic types, is in the teeth, which in the former are more firmly fastened into the jaws. Mammals make further improvements in teeth. They usually have two successive sets and have enamel-covered surfaces which effectively grind up hard terrestrial plants. Birds in modern times all have horny beaks which tear flesh, strain small organisms from water, or crack hard seeds of vascular plants. Their gizzards grind up resistant foods.

The animals which have taken advantage of the food resources on land, though consuming a great variety of foods, are on the whole representatives of a few specialized groups which by particular adaptations have taken advantage of the great stores of organic foods in land vegetation.

Acclimatization

Animals which change from one habitat to another must acquire new ranges of toleration for environmental factors. The degree of acclimatization that an animal undergoes may be judged by changes in its ability to survive extreme conditions, by its success in populating new habitats, or its behavior after being subjected to changed conditions (Shelford, 1929). The reason why the majority of terrestrial animals have reached land through the fresh waters rather than directly from the sea is in part due to the favorable series of intermediate environments (Carter, 1931). The adaptations are acquired serially, and thus more easily. The mechanisms for acclimatization appear to be concerned with modifications in the character of protoplasms. At times they may be shown to consist of loss of water, changes in metabolic rate, or other measurable variations, but the factors concerned in many of them are still unknown.

Animals which have entered brackish water from either sea water or fresh water may be small in size (Schlieper, 1933). In some of these, oxygen consumption may decrease as much as 25%. The activity of surface membranes and excretory organs may be inhibited. Other animals that readily adjust themselves to changed salinities usually use more oxygen in diluted sea water for a time, and may become more or less "febrile." A marine animal that migrates from the ocean into fresher water needs more energy and, if it cannot supply it, is inhibited in various ways. Gunter (1947) claims that marine animals tend to grow smaller in lower salinities. Andrews (1925) tested the resistance of sixteen species of littoral animals to variations in temperature, acidity, salinity, stagnation, and light. He found that young animals usually died more quickly than old when there were extreme variations, but that the former had greater capacity for acclimatization if changes were gradual. Young animals probably died quickly on account of their surface-mass relations and more rapid metabolism. Old animals were less resistant to acidity, probably on account of a more limited alkali reserve.

Growth is probably an autocatalytic process (Robertson, 1923). Its rate changes abruptly at certain critical temperatures (Crozier, 1929) and in response to other environmental changes. Hence variations in an animal's environment may cause changes in metabolism, lack of growth, or death. Rate of growth and metabolic activity commonly change with age (Burge, 1921). Variations in temperature alter equilibrium constants of chemical reactions and the relative proportions of reacting materials. It is therefore usually easier for an animal to adjust its activities to a lower than to a higher temperature (Wardlaw, 1931). As would be expected, aquatic animals vary greatly in their ability to resist the extreme variations in temperature, salinity, and other factors which accompany landward migrations. Starfish larvae do not have much ability to adjust themselves to higher temperatures, but ciliates do (Jacobs, 1919). A fish consumes three times as much food at 20°C. as at 10°C. (Hathaway, 1927). Animals can, if subjected to altered environmental conditions, alter their range of activities to some extent, i.e., they become acclimatized to new levels (Davenport, 1908; Huntsman, 1924a, 1924b; Gompel & Legendre, 1927). As time for its metamorphosis approaches, a toad tadpole loses much of its ability to endure high temperatures (Hathaway, 1928). As it prepares for land life, it acquires new powers and loses old abilities. Adjustments usually involve such compensations in the way of acquisitions and losses.

Acclimatizations often result in rhythmical adjustments to regularly recurring variations in environment. As such variations are more extreme in land and fresh-water habitats than in the sea, animals in the former generally show more striking adjustments than those in the latter. The differences between the habits of nocturnal and diurnal animals, for example, are on the whole greater among land animals than among those in the ocean. When the environment is most variable, ranges of physiological endurance and adjustment are usually wider. Under such circumstances it is not strange that homoiothermic animals, while they enjoy the stimulating uncertainty of life on land, have attained some degree of stability by having constancy in internal fluids which bathe living cells and in body temperatures.

Kennedy (1925) has "come across two species of insects, one a dragonfly, the other a mayfly, in which a reversal of one or more of the tropisms normal to the other species of the same genus has permitted the entrance of these reversal species into environments not open to normal members of the genus." These insects have made adjustments which have given them special advantages by forsaking traditional modes of behavior for their types.

Acclimatizations may be concerned with resistance, toleration, enlarged or restricted ranges of adjustment, changing tropisms and habits, or other things. They usually involve complex groups of activities, but the net results permit animals to live in a changed environment.

Parasites

In the ocean many animals are associated with others as commensals, symbionts, or parasites, but such relations are not usually carried over into fresh-water and land habitats. Parasites show a general tendency to become specialists in their host relations. Many are restricted to a single species, genus, or family, though there are also numerous wide-ranging types. Parasites are often used as indicators of the past history and relationships of their hosts (Metcalf, 1929).

Parasites that occur in and out of the water along shore are of special interest in connection with aboceanic migrations. In such widely separated localities as the coasts of China, Japan, and Dry Tortugas (Pearse, 1929, 1930a, 1931) the land crabs along shore carry more parasites than crabs in the ocean. Some of the terrestrial parasites (mites) evidently were acquired on land, but even such types as certain species of parasitic copepods (Wilson, 1913; Pearse, 1930b) and commensal vorticellids (Pearse, 1930a, 1932c) are seldom found on aquatic crustaceans and are quite common on terrestrial types because the bloods of such hosts are more stable and nutritious than those of their more primitive relatives in the ocean, but the consistent presence of others is not so easy to explain. In Japan a rather careful survey of the parasites of eight species of salamanders which ranged from aquatic to terrestrial types showed some peculiar anomalies which were apparently due more to host specificities than to habitat relations (Pearse, 1932f). Among protozoans: Trypanosoma and Balantidium were found only in an aquatic newt; Trichodina only in the bladder of a land salamander that bred in water; and Opalina and Endamoeba in a land salamander. Amphistomes, distomes, and Rhabdias were found only in aquatic salamanders; Gorgoderina and cestode cysts were found only in terrestrial salamanders. At the mouth of the Menam Chao Phya in Siam the aquatic crabs had more parasites than those on land, largely because two species of large portunids often had their gill-cavities filled with barnacles (Pearse, 1933a); the land gobies also had fewer and different types of parasites from those that lived in the river itself (Pearse, 1933). The writer has spent several years trying to discover significant differences between the parasites of related aquatic and terrestrial animals. A few facts have been discovered, but on the whole the results are as yet disappointing, perhaps largely on account of host specificity. More work is needed.

Conclusion

Animals that have left the stability of the ocean for the greater environmental instability that obtains to some extent in fresh water and to a greater degree on land have been obliged to modify their internal organizations to keep pace with external changes. Their skins have grown more selective in permitting or preventing the passage of solutes and finally have been modified to conserve body water and regulate temperature. Respiratory organs have changed so that breathing has been transferred from external water-bathed gills to internal, moist pulmonary cavities. Body fluids have changed from salty solutions closely resembling sea water to hypertonic but less saline, nutritious, viscid, gas-transporting media which maintain standard and rather constant concentrations. Metabolism has come under the control of many regulatory mechanisms and on the whole proceeds more rapidly. Land animals generally live faster than aquatic animals, partly because they have continual access to large amounts of oxygen and partly because they live in a more changeful, and therefore a more stimulating, environment. Fresh-water animals generally live faster than marine animals because they con-

tinually have to expend energy to maintain the osmotic equilibrium of their internal fluids. Locomotion has become swifter, better controlled, and more purposeful. The nervous system has acquired better correlating mechanisms and greater centralization of control. The sense organs have become better adapted for distance perception, and less dependence is placed on contact sensations in making rapid adjustments to changes in environment. Excretory organs which perhaps began as regulators of osmotic pressure have taken over the elimination of metabolic waste products, especially those containing nitrogen. Reproductive functions have been improved and adapted by internal fertilization; protection of young from thermal changes, desiccation, and other dangers; and by the nourishment, care, and education of the young. Adaptations have been developed for the utilization of the great food resources in land habitats; especially the products of hard, but concentrated and nutritious, vascular plants. Through slow acclimatization to new conditions animals have changed from sluggish systems of activities in a uniform environment where little energy is available to active, speedy systems. Land animals by keeping their internal mechanisms uniform and by moving at a rapid metabolic rate are able to live successfully in a variable environment where much energy is available.

Fig. 23. A sandy shore at Portsmouth in Dominica. Home of the ghost crab and other burrowers which are gradually emigrating toward land. (Photo by R. E. Blackwelder.)

5

WHAT ANIMALS HAVE ATTAINED ON LAND

ONLY one-fifth of the species of animals on the earth are aquatic (Harms, 1929). Though conditions of life on land are in some respects severe, they appear to have been, and are today, favorable for the formation of new species. Animals which have struggled up the long evolutionary trail from marine and fresh-water habitats and stand today on dry land are the dominant ones of the earth. They are the successful. What is success? Has the struggle been justified?

Success is continual improvement (Pearse, 1926a). It is the result of competition for a place to live. There are of course various degrees of success. The mere fact that an animal is alive is a certification that it is to some degree successful. Among land animals, ants exceed all other types combined in individuals (Wheeler, 1910). They are successful and dominant among those which have attained land because they are progressive yet generalized. Ants are active, keen of sense, modern, and so progressive that they have built up a social organization that has long excited wonder and admiration among successful, dominant, and social vertebrates. Yet ants have not generally limited their food to one or two peculiar substances as the honey bee has, and they have not lost the thermal and aqueous stability that goes with close association with soil. A successful animal is both plastic and progressive. It must always live in the world as it is and to some extent do such living with greater efficiency than its rivals.

Animals which struggle may look down with more or less contempt on those which are able, by lurking in the crevices or the slack waters of evolutionary currents, to find soft berths where they may exist without a struggle. Such degenerates pay the penalty exacted by the Gods of Biology. When they cease to struggle, they lose their abilities—they not only retrogress in power, but also lose appreciation. Every barnacle starts in life as a free-swimming nauplius with eyes and other sense organs. Barnacles which settle on rocks along shore to enjoy life, where waves and tide perennially insure food and certain favorable conditions of life, lose their eyes, and thus to some degree their power to appreciate things outside themselves. Barnacles which go farther down the road which leads from struggle likewise start in life as apperceptive nauplei; but they attach themselves, not to sturdy rocks, but to other animals and lose all semblance to struggling crustaceans. As adults, they are rotund masses without legs or sense organs. They send root-like absorptive organs into their unlucky hosts and thus steal food; their bodies become soft sacs which produce myriads of eggs. They have a certain success—they continue to live, but they are degraded, specialized, and limited. Land animals because they live in a changeful environment are stimulated to be alert strugglers.

If it is desirable to move speedily and handle problems encountered in environment with increasing understanding and efficiency, to be progressive, then the struggle to land has been worth while. Speed is a primary quality of land animals (Jehu, 1923). They live in a rarer medium than aquatic animals, and in the atmosphere an abundance of oxygen for metabolic activity permits them to live faster (Krogh, 1916). Fast living requires a continual supply of nutritious food, which is available in land plants, and for terrestrial animals this is supplemented by a greater quantity of radiant energy than is to be had in aquatic habitats. Kennedy (1928) has pointed out that insects are generally distributed in relation to available energy according to their degree of specialization. The primitive insects frequent moist places close to the soil and are often nocturnal; specialized insects fly in the open sunlight when time of day and season of year make most energy available.

One quality of terrestrial environment is variability. This has been a factor in the development of that most effective adaptation to land life—homoiothermism. Birds and mammals, which keep their body temperatures and their body fluids close to optimum conditions for cell activity, are so independent of environment that they can, if stored energy is available in the form of food, live in polar regions and tropical deserts where life is impossible for poikilothermic land animals. Homoiothermism makes continuity of activity and thoughtful endeavor possible.

The variability of land habitats stimulates animals to greater versatility in response to environmental changes. It is on land that animals have developed greatest ability to solve complex problems. The most astute thinkers are land animals. Even on land monotony is conducive to lack of progressive accomplishment. Man has not done his greatest works in the tropics, where much radiant energy is available and temperatures are always high. Conditions of life are too monotonous. The most progressive modern races and nations are found in temperate regions where humidities and temperatures vary. In such localities men are most healthy, competent, and productive (Huntington, 1927).

Perhaps the fairest flower of progressive evolutionary growth on land is human civilization. This is the product of homoiothermism, which permits continuity of activity, social life, which multiplies and strengthens individual accomplishment and, by the overlapping of generations and the accumulation of works in the way of social procedures, homes, inventions, libraries, etc., also contributes to continuity of cumulative activity. Man through knowledge has means for controlling environment or compensating for changes in it. Such extra-corporal assets are far above those at the command of any other animal. He is able more or less to keep conditions outside his body stable. Civilized life thus tends to become monotonous, and man suffers ennui. He yearns for excitement. A savage is continually busy escaping dangers and finding enough to eat. A civilized man has leisure, which is a luxury that only a few animals enjoy. How man shall spend his leisure time is perhaps the chief problem of organized human society today. Civilization and social life has perhaps become too much a matter of "being in style." A child spends years being educated to know what others know and to behave like others. Civilization becomes more and more a matter of drinking coffee, smoking cigarettes, and seeing moving pictures or baseball games. Joad (1928) compares man to a child with a box of matches—science has given him leisure, and he does not have wisdom enough to know what to do with it. The reason is that knowledge and opportunity have not changed the primitive nature of man (Schiller, 1924). The quick and astute continue to exploit the slow and unprogressive. Abilities differ and all cannot be reduced to a common level. If one man elects in his spare hours to improve his abilities by study or practice, society should reward him. Another man who chooses to sit in idleness or waste himself by keeping busy with the trivialities of life should be penalized. Organized work is a product of society. It is today the best tool which may contribute to the attainment of success. But it must not be just work, such as satisfies industrious natures; it must be thoughtful and purposeful work.

BIBLIOGRAPHY

Abel, O.

1919. Die Stämme der Wirbeltiere. Berlin und Leipzig, xviii + 914.

1922. Lebensbilder aus der Tierwelt der Vorzeit. Jena, vii + 639.

1924. Lehrbuch der Paläozoologie. Jena, xiv + 523.

1925. Geschichte und Methode der Rekonstruction vorzeitblecher Wirbeltiere. Jena, viii + 327.

1929. Paläobiologie und Stammesgeschichte. Jena, x + 323.

Acloque, A.

1911. Crabes terrestres. Cosmos, Paris, 64:11-13.

Adamstone, F. B.

1924. The bottom fauna of Lake Nipigon. Univ. Toronto Stud. Biol. 24:43-70.

1924a. The distribution and economic importance of the bottom fauna of Lake Nipigon with an appendix of the bottom fauna of Lake Ontario. *Ibid.* 24:33-100.

Adamstone, F. B., & Harkness, W. J. K.

1923. The bottom organisms of Lake Nipigon. Univ. Toronto Stud., Fish. Lab. 22: 121-170.

Adolph, E. F.

1925. Some physiological distinctions between freshwater and marine organisms. Biol. Bull. 48:327-335.

1927. The regulation of volume and concentration in the body fluids of earthworms. J. Exper. Zool. 47:105-149.

1927a. Changes in body volume in several species of larval Amphibia in relation to the osmotic pressure of the environment. *Ibid.* 47:163-178.

1927b. Changes in the physiological regulation of body volume in Rana pipiens during ontogeny and metamorphosis. *Ibid.* 47:179-195.

1927c. The process of adaptation to salt solutions in frogs. *Ibid.* 49:321-351.

1927d. The skin and kidneys as regulators of body volume in frogs. *Ibid.* 47:1-30.

1927e. The excretion of water by the kidneys of frogs. Am. J. Physiol. 81:315-324.

1929. How the skin equilibrates the water content and the osmotic pressure of frogs. *Ibid.* 90:260.

1931. The water exchanges of frogs with and without skin. *Ibid.* 96:569-586.

1931a. The size of the body and the size of the environment in the growth of tadpoles. Biol. Bull. 61:350-375.

1932. The vapor tension relations of frogs. *Ibid.* 67:112-125.

1933. Exchanges of water in the frog. Biol. Rev. 8:224-240.

1943. Physiological regulations. Lancaster, Pa., xvi + 502.

Adolph, E. F. & P. E.

1925. The regulation of body volume in freshwater organisms. J. Exper. Zool 43:105-149.

Agersborg, H. P. K.
1927. The distribution, variation, and evolution of certain prosobranchiate Mollusca from the littoral zone of the coasts of New Zealand and Norway. Anat. Rec. 37:149.

Alcock, A.
1902. A Naturalist in Indian Seas. London, xxiv + 328 pp. 98 figs., 1 map.
1910. Catalogue of the Indian Decapod Crustacea in the Collection of the Indian Museum. Pt. 1, Brachyura Fas. II, the Indian Fresh-water Crabs—Potamonidae. Ann. Mag. Nat. Hist. (8) 6:440.

Alcock, A., & Anderson, A. R.
1894. List of the shore- and shallow-water Brachyura collected during the season 1893-1894. J. Asiatic Soc. of Bengal 63:197-209.

Alexander, G.
1932. An instance of the importance of H+-ion control in osmo-regulation studies. Ecology 13:101-102.

Alexander, W. B., Southgate, B: A., & Bassindale, R.
1932. The salinity of the water retained in the muddy foreshore of an estuary. J. Marine Biol. Assn. U. K. 18:297-298.

Allee, W. C.
1923. Studies in marine ecology. I. The distribution of common littoral invertebrates of the Woods Hole region. Biol. Bull. 44:167-191.
1923a. Studies in marine ecology. III. Some physical factors related to the distribution of littoral invertebrates. *Ibid.* 44:205-253.
1923b. Studies in marine ecology. IV. The effect of the temperature in limiting the geographical range of invertebrates of the Woods Hole littoral. Ecology 4:341-354.

Allen, E. J.
1923. The progression of life in the sea. Rep. Brit. Assn. London 90:79-93.

Allison, J. B., & Cole, W. H.
1932. Stimulation in Fundulus by hydrochloric and fatty acids at different hydrogen-ion concentrations in sea water. Anat. Rec. 54:67.

Alluaud, C.
1926. Observations sur la faune entomologique intercotidale. Bull. Soc. Zool. France 51(2):152-154.

Amemiya, I.
1928. Ecological studies of Japanese oysters with special reference to the salinity of their habitats. J. Col. Agr. Imp. Univ. Tokyo 9:333-382.

Anderson, A. R.
1894. Note on the Sound produced by the Ocypode crab, *Ocypode ceratophthalma.* J. Asiatic Soc. Bengal 63:138-139.

Andrews, C. W.
1900. A monograph of Christmas Island. London, xv + 337.
1910. The habits of the robber crab. Proc. Zool. Soc. London (1909): 887-889.

Andrews, F. B.
1925. The resistance of marine animals of different ages. Publ. Puget Sd. Biol. Sta. 3:361-363.

Andrusov, N.

1897. Fossile und lebende Dreissensidae Eurasiens. Trudy St. Peterb. Obsschestest. 25:1-681.

Annandale, N.

1907. The fauna of brackish ponds at Port Canning, Lower Bengal. Part III. An isolated race of the actinian *Metridium schillerianum* (Stoliczka). Rec. Indian Mus. 1:47-74.

1909. The habits of king crabs. *Ibid.* 3:294-295.

1922. The marine element in the fauna of the Ganges. Bijdr. Dierk. Amsterdam (Feest-Num., M. Weber): 143-154.

Arcongeli, A.

1927. Revisione del generi degli isopodi terrestri. I. Nota. Sopra aleuni generi di Africa e di America. Atti. Soc. Ital. Sci. Nat. e Mus. Civico Storia Nat. Milano 66:126-141.

Arey, L. B., & Crozier, W. J.

1921. Natural history of Onchidium. J. Exper. Zool. 32:433-502.

Arnett, R. H., Jr.

1950. Notes on the distribution, habits, and habitats of some Panama culicines (Diptera, Culicidae). J. N. Y. Entomol. Soc. 58:99-115.

Atkins, W. R. G.

1917. Osmotic pressure in animals and plants. Sci. Progr. 11:562-577.

1922. The hydrogen ion concentration of sea water in its biological relations. J. Mar. Biol. Assn. Plymouth 12:717-771.

Ayers, J. C.

1938. Relationship of habitat to oxygen consumption in certain estuarine crabs. Ecology 19:522-527.

Babcock, S. M.

1912. Metabolic water: its production and rôle in vital phenomena. Univ. Wis. Agr. Exp. Stat., Research Bull. 22, 87-181.

Backer, C. A.

1930. The problem of Krakatao as seen by a botanist. Hague 1-299.

Bailey, J. L.

1929. Freshwater Mollusca in brackish water. Nautilus 43:34.

Baldwin, Ernest

1937. An introduction to comparative biochemistry. N .Y. xviii + 112.

Baldwin, F. M.

1924. Comparative rates of oxygen consumption in marine forms. Proc. Iowa Acad. Sci. 30:173-180.

Ballantyne, F. M.

1927. Air bladder and lungs. Trans. Roy. Soc. Edinburgh 55:371-394.

Balss, H.

1922. Ostasiatische Decapoden. III. Die Dromiaceen, Oxystomen, und Parthenopiden. Arch. f. Naturges. 88:104-140.

1922a. Ostasiatische Decapoden. IV. Die Branchyrhynchen (Cancridea). *Ibid.* 88:141-166.

1930. Wanderung bei Decapoden (Crustaceen). Ergeb. Biol. 6:305-326.

Banta, A. M.

1907. The fauna of Mayfield's Cave. Publ. Carnegie Inst. Washington 67:1-114.

Barnes, T. C.

1932. Salt requirements and space orientation of the littoral isopod Ligia in Bermuda. Biol. Bull. 63:496-504.

1932a. The physiological effect of trihydrol in water. P. Nat. Acad. Sci. 18:136-137.

Barrell, J.

1916. Influence of Climates on Vertebrates. Bull. Geol. Soc. of Amer. 27:40-41; 387-436.

1917. Probable relations of climatic change to the origin of the tertiary ape man. Sci. Mo. 4:16-26.

Barrell, J., Schuchert, C., Woodruff, L. L., Lull, R. S., and Huntington, E.

1924. The evolution of the earth and its inhabitants. New Haven, xiv + 207.

Baskerville, M. L.

1927. The permeability of frog skin to urea. I. The influence of NaCl and $CaCl_2$. Biol. Bull. 53:239-246.

1927. The permeability of frog skin to urea. II. The effect of dextrose and sucrose. *Ibid.* 53:247-257.

Bassindale, R.

1942. The distribution of amphipods in the Severn Estuary and Bristol Channel. J. Animal Ecol. 11:131-144.

Batchelder, C. H.

1926. An ecological study of a brackish-water stream. Ecology 7:55-71.

Bateman, J. B.

1933. Osmotic and ionic regulation in the shore crab, *Carcinas maenas,* with notes on the blood concentrations of *Gammarus locusta* and *Ligia oceanica.* J. Exper. Biol. 10:355-371.

Bateman, J. B., & Keys, A.

1932. Chloride and vapour-pressure relations in the secretory activity of the gills of the eel. J. Physiol. 75:226-240.

Baumberger, J. P., & Olmsted, J. M. D.

1928. Changes in the osmotic pressure and water content of crabs during the molt cycle. Physiol. Zool. 1:531-544.

Baumeister, L.

1913. Über die Augen der Schlammspringer (Periophthalmus und Boleophthalmus). Zool. Jahrb., Anat. 35:340-354.

Baylis, H. A.

1915. A parasitic oligochaete and other inhabitants of the gill-chambers of land crabs. Ann. Mag. Nat. Hist. (8) 15:378-381.

Beadle, L. C.

1931. The effect of salinity changes on the water content and respiration of marine invertebrates. J. Exper. Biol. 8:211-227.

1932. Observations on the bionomics of some East African swamps. J. Linn. Soc. 38:135-156.

1932a. The waters of some East African lakes in relation to their fauna and flora. *Ibid.* 38:157-212.

1934. Osmotic regulation in *Gunda ulvae.* J. Exper. Biol. 11:382-396.

1943. An ecological survey of some inland saline waters of Algeria. J. Linn. Soc. London 41:218-242.

Beattie, Mary V. F.

1932. The physico-chemical factors of water in relation to mosquito breeding in Trinidad. Bull. Ent. Res. London 23(4):477-500. 2 pl., 11 fig.

Beebe, C. W. & M. B.

1909. A Naturalist in the Tropics. Harpers Mag. 118:590-600.

Beer, T.

1894. Die Accomodation des Fischauges. Arch. ges. Physiol. 58:523-650.

Behre, E. H.

1918. An experimental study of acclimation to temperature in *Planaria dorotocephala.* Biol. Bull. 35:277-317.

Bell, H. P.

1927. Observations on the seasonal disappearance of certain marine algae in the tide pools near the biological station, St. Andrew's, New Brunswick. Proc. and Tr. Nova Scotian Inst. Sci. 17:1-5.

Benedict, F. G.

1932. The physiology of large reptiles, with special reference to heat production of snakes, tortoises, lizards and alligators. Pub. Carnegie Inst. Wash. 425: x + 539.

Benham, W. B.

1901. Polychaet worms. Camb. Nat. Hist. 3:241-346.

Berger, Eva

1930. Unterschiedliche Wirkungen gleiches Sonen & Sonengemische auf Verschiedene Tierarten. (Ein Beitrag für Lehre Ion Sonenantagonismus.) Pflüger's Archiv. 223:1-39.

Berry, E. W.

1920. The evolution of flowering plants and warmblooded animals. Am. J. Sci. (4)49:207-211.

1925. The environment of early vertebrates. Amer. Nat. 59:354-362.

1929. Paleontology. N. Y., xii + 392.

Bertin, L.

1920. Les grenouilles peuvent elles se adapter à l'eau saumâtre? C. R. Soc. Biol. Paris 83:1308-1309.

Bethe, A.

1897. Das Nervensystem von *Carcinas maenas.* Ein Anatomisch-physiologischer Versuch. 1. Theil. -1. Mittheilung. Arch. f. Mikr. Anat. 50:460-546.

1927. Der Einfluss der Ionen des Seewassers auf rhythmische Bewegungen von Meerestieren. Arch. ges. Physiol. 217:456-468.

1929. Über die Permeabilität der Korperoberflächen von Seetieren. Amer. J. Physiol. 90:283-284.

Bews, J. W.

1923. Notes on the evolution of plant growth forms. So. Afr. Jr. Sci. 20:290-303.

1925. Plant forms and their evolution in South Africa. Review. Jour. Ecol. 14:167-168.

1927. Studies in the ecological evolution of the Angiosperms. London, viii + 134.

Bialaszewwicz, K.

1932. Sur la régulation de la composition minérale de l'hemolymphe chez le Crabe. Archiv Internat. Physiol. 35:98-100.

Bigelow, H. B.

1931. Oceanography; its scope, problems, and economic importance. Boston, vii + 263.

Bigelow, H. B., & Edmondson, W. T.

1947. Wind waves at sea; breakers and surf. U. S. Hydrogr. Office. No. 602: xii + 177.

Black, Virginia S.

1948. Changes in density, weight, chloride, and swimbladder gas in the killifish, *Fundulus heteroditus*, in fresh water and sea water. Biol. Bull. 95:83-93.

Blanchard, F. N.

1930. The stimulus to the breeding migration of the spotted salamander, *Ambystoma maculatum* (Shaw). Amer. Nat. 64:154-167.

Blegvad, H.

1914. Food and conditions of nourishment among the communities of invertebrate animals on or in the sea bottom in Danish waters. Danish Biol. Sta. Rept. 22:41-78.

1916. On the food of fish in the Danish waters within the Skew. *Ibid*. 24:17-72.

1925. Continued studies on the quantity of fish-food on the sea bottom. *Ibid*. 31:27-76.

Blum, H. F.

1922. On the effect of low salinity on *Teredo navalis*. Univ. Cal. Publ. Zool. 22:349-368.

Blumenthal, R.

1927. A micro blood sugar method and the blood sugars of insects. Science 65:617-619.

Bodine, J. H.

1923. Hibernation in Orthoptera. I. Physiological changes during hibernation in certain Orthoptera. J. Exper. Zool. 37:457-476.

1928. Action of salts on Fundulus egg. Biol. Bull. 54:396-404.

1929. Factors influencing the rate of respiratory metabolism of a developing egg (Orthoptera). Physiol. Zool. 2:459-482.

Bohn, G., and Drzewina, A.

1925. Au sujet de la régulation du pH de l'eau de mer. C. R. Soc. Biol. Paris 93:917-919.

Bond, R. M.

1932. Observations on *Artemia "francescana"* Kellogg, especially on the relation of environment to morphology, Internat. Rev. gesamt. Hydro-biol. u. Hygrogr. 28:117-125.

1933. A contribution to the study of the natural foodcycle in aquatic environments. Bull. Bingham Oceanogr. Col. Peabody Mus. Nat. Hist. Yale Univ. 4(4): 1-89.

Bond, R. M., Cary, M. K., & Hutchinson, G. E.

1932. A note on the blood of the hog-fish, *Polistotrema stouti* (Lockington). J. Exper. Biol. 9:12-14.

Bornebusch, C. H.

1930. The fauna of forest soil. Forstlige Forsgv. Danmark 11:1-225, 28 pls.

Borcea, I.

1926. Observations sur la faune des lacs Razelm. Ann. Sci. Univ. Jassy 13:424-448.

1931. Quelques élémentes de la faune de pénétration dans les eaux douces sur le littoral Roumain de la Mer Noire. Arch. Zool. Ital. 16:661-662.

Borradaile, L. A.

1900. On the young of the robber crab. Zool. Results Willey Pt. 5:586-590.

1903. Land Crustaceans. Fauna and Geogr. of Maldive and Laccadive Archipel. 1:64-100.

1923. The animal and its environment. London, vii + 399.

Borsuk, V., & Kreps, E.

1929. Untersuchungen über den respiratorischen Gaswechsel bei Balanus balanoides und Balanus crenatus bei verschiedenem Salzgehalt des Aussenmilieus. III. Mitteilung. Über den Sauerstoffverbrauch im Luftmilieu bei verschiedenem Salzgehalt der Körperflüssigkeiten bei Balanus balanoides. Arch. ges. Phys. 222:371-380.

Borza, A., & Bujorean, G.

1927. Contributional experimentale la cunoasterea problemei originei florelor insulare. Bul. Gradinii Bot. Mus. Bot. Univ. Cluj. 6:49-56.

Bower, F. O.

1908. The origin of a land flora. London, xii + 727.

1929. The origin of a land flora, 1908-1929. *Ibid*, 1-27.

Bramlette, M. N.

1926. Some marine bottom samples from Pago Pago Harbor, Samoa. Carnegie Inst. Washington Publ. 344:3-35.

Brandt, K.

1896. Das vordringen mariner Thiere in dem Kaiser Wilhelm-Canal. Zool. Jahrb., Syst. 9:387-408.

Breder, C. M.

1933. The significance of Ca to marine fishes on invading fresh water. Anat. Rec. 57:57.

Bridge, T. W.

1904. Fishes. Cambr. Nat. Hist. 7:139-537.

Brighenti, D.

1929. Richerche biologiche sulle volli salse della Mesola. Boll. Pesca, Piscicolt. e. Idrobiol., Roma 55:492-537.

Brock, F.

1926. Das Verhalten des Einsiedlerkrebses, *Pagurus arrosor* Herbst, während der Suche und Aufnahme der Nahrung. Zeitschr. Morphol. Ökol. Tiere 6: 415-552.

1930. Das Verhalten der ersten Antennen von Brachyuren und Anomuren in Bezug auf das umgebende Medium. Zeitschr. Wiss. Biol. Abt. C. Zeitschr. Vergleich. Physiol. 11:774-790.

Brooks, W. K.

1894. The origin of the oldest fossils and the discovery of the bottom of the ocean. J. Geol. 2:455-479.

Brody, S.

1928. A comparison of growth curves of man and other animals. Science 67:43-46.

Bruce, J. R.

1924. A pH method for determining the carbon dioxide changes of marine, brackish-water, and freshwater organisms. British J. Exper. Biol. 2:57-64.

1928. Physical factors on the sandy beach. Part I. Tidal, climatic, and edaphic. J. Marine Biol. Assoc. United Kingdom 15:535-565.

Brues, C. T.

1927. Occurrence of the marine crab, *Callinectes ornatus,* in brackish and fresh water. Amer. Nat. 61:566-569.

1927a. Animal life in hot springs. Q. Rev. Biol. 2:181-203.

1928. Studies on the fauna of hot springs in the Western United States and the biology of thermophilous animals. P. Am. Acad. Arts & Sci. 63:139-228.

Brunelli, G. e Maldura

1929. Osservazioni sul lago di Pergusa. Boll. Pesca, Piscicolt. e Idrobiol. 5:596-604.

Bryan, W. A.

1915. Natural history of Hawaii. Honolulu, 1-596.

Bryce, D.

1925. The Rotifera and Gastrotricha of Devil's and Stump Lakes, North Dakota, U. S. A. J. Quekett. Micros. cl. London, 15:81-108.

Buckle, P.

1923. On the ecology of soil insects on agricultural land. J. Ecol. 11:93-102.

Burge, W. E. & E. L.
1921. An explanation for the variation in the intensity of oxidation in the life cycle. J. Exper. Zool. 32:203-206.

Burgess, G. K.
1924. Standard density and volumetric tables. 6 Ed. U. S. Dept. Com., Circ. Bu. Stand. 19:1-72.

Burollet, P. A.
1926. Considérations dynamogénétique sur le "salicornietum" de quelques sebkhas tunisiennes. C. R. Assoc. Franç. Avanc. Sci. 49:352-355.

Bury, H.
1895. The metamorphosis of echinoderms. Q. J. Microscop Sci. 38:45-135.

Buxton, P. A.
1923. Animal life in deserts: a study of the fauna in relation to environment. London, xv + 176.
1926. The colonization of the sea by insects. Proc. Zool. Soc. London (1926): 807-814.
1930. Evaporation from the mealworm (Tenebrio: Coleoptera) and atmospheric humidity Proc. Roy. Soc. London 106:560-577.
1931. The thermal death-point of Rhodnius (Rhynchota, Heteroptera) under controlled conditions of humidity. J. Exper. Biol. 8:275-278.

Cahn, A. R.
1925. The migration of animals. Amer. Nat. 59:539-556.

Caldwell, G. T.
1927. A new apparatus for quantitative determinations of the respiratory exchange of very small mammals. Anat. Rec. 37:137.

Calman, W. T.
1909. Crustacea. Lankester's Treatise on Zoology 7(3):viii + 346.

Cameron, A. E.
1913. General survey of the insect fauna of the soil within a limited area near Manchester; a consideration of the relationships between soil insects and the physical conditions of their habitat. J. Econ. Biol. 8:159-204.

Cameron, A. T., & Mounce, I.
1922. Some physical and chemical factors influencing the distribution of marine flora and fauna in the Strait of Georgia and adjacent waters. Contrib. Canadian Biol. 1:39-70.

Campbell, D. A.
1930. The origin of land plants. Science 72:177-187.

Cannon, H. G.
1923. A note on the zoaea of a landcrab, *Cardisoma armatum*. Proc. Zool. Soc. London (1923):11-14.

Carter, G. S.
1931. Aquatic and aerial respiration in animals. Biol. Rev. 6:1-35.

Carter, G. S., & Beadle, L. C.
1930. The fauna of the swamps of the Paraguayan Chaco in relation to its environment. I. Physico-chemical nature of the environment. J. Linn. Soc. London, Zool. 37:205-258.

1931. The fauna of the swamps of the Paraguayan Chaco in relation to its environment. II. Respiratory adaptations in the fishes. *Ibid.* 37:327-368.

1931a. The fauna of the swamps of the Paraguayan Chaco in relation to its environment. III. Respiratory adaptations in the Oligochaeta. *Ibid.* 37: 379-386.

Case, E. C.

1919. The environment of vertebrate life in the late paleozoic in North America: a palaeogeographical study. Carnegie Inst. Washington Publ. 283:vii + 273.

1926. Environment of tetrapod life in the late paleozoic of regions other than North America. *Ibid.* 375:iv + 211.

Caullery, M.

1929. Effects des grands froids sur les organismes de la zone intercotidale dans le Boulounais. Bull. Soc. Zool. France 54:267-269.

Chaisson, A. F.

1930. The changes in the blood concentration of *Raja erinacea* produced by modification of the salinity of the external medium. Contr. Canadian Biol. and Fish. 5(18):475-484.

Chamberlin, T. C., & Salisbury, R. D.

1905. Geology. 2:xxvi + 692.

Chapman, R. C.

1931. Animal ecology, with especial reference to insects. N. Y., x + 464.

Chater, E. H.

1927. On the distribution of the larger brown algae in Aberdeenshire estuaries. Tr. and Proc. Bot. Soc. Edinburgh 29:362-380.

Cheesman, L. E.

1922. Observations on the land crab, *Cardisoma armatum,* with especial regard to sense organs. Proc. Zool. Soc. London (1922):361-363.

1923. Notes on the pairing of the land-crab, Cardisoma armatum. *Ibid.* (1923): 173.

Chidester, F. E.

1916. The influence of salinity on the development of certain species of mosquito larvae and its bearing on the problem of distribution of species. New Jersey Agr. Exper. Sta. Bull. 299:1-16.

1922. Studies on fish migration. II. The influence of salinity on the dispersal of fishes. Amer. Nat. 56:373-380.

1924. A critical examination of the evidence for physical and chemical influences on fish migration. British J. Exper. Biol. 2:79-118.

Church, A. H.

1919. The building of an autotrophic flagellate. Bot. Mem. Oxford 1:1-27.

1921. The lichen as a transmigrant. J. Bot. 59:1-13, 40-46.

1926. Reproductive mechanism in land flora. J. Bot. 64:33-40, 99-103, 132-136.

1926a. Reproductive mechanism in land flora. V. Sporangia. *Ibid.* 64:234-240; 257-262. VI. Sporaphylls. *Ibid.* 64: 307-310; 332-336.

Clark, A. H.

1925. Life in the ocean. Ann. Rept. Smithsonian Inst. (1923):369-394.

1927. Geography and zoology. Ann. Assoc. Amer. Geogr. 17:102-145.

Clark, J. H.

1922. The physiological action of light. Physiol. Rev. 2:277-309.

Clarke, F. W., & Wheeler, W. C.

1917. The inorganic constituents of marine invertebrates. Prof. Pap. U. S. Geol. Surv. Washington 102:1-56.

Cole, W. H.

1929. The relation between temperature and the pedal rhythm of Balanus. J. Gen. Physiol. 12:599-608.

Colgan, N.

1910. Notes on the adaptability of certain littoral Mollusca. Irish Nat. 19:127-133.

Colman, J.

1933. Intertidal zonation. J. Mar. Biol. Assn. United King. 18:435-476.

Colosi, G.

1926. Remarques sur le peuplement des terres. C. R. Assoc. Franç. Avanc. Sci. 49:728-733.

1927. Il popolamento delle terre emerse e i fattori delle grande transmigrazioni. Universo (Firenze) 8(4):359-373.

1930. Il medium respiratio. Riv. Patol. Sperim. 5:72-80.

Condorelli, L.

1928. Ricerche sulla pressione osmotica del sangue in alcuni pesci del Golfo di Napoli. Boll. Soc. Ital. Biol. Sper. 3:197-203.

Conrad, H. S., & Galligar, G. C.

1929. Third survey of a Long Island salt marsh. Ecology 10:326-333.

Conway, E. J.

1945. The physiological significance of inorganic levels in the internal medium of animals. Biol. Rev. 20:56-72.

Cort, W. W.

1928. Abstracts of papers contributed to the fourth annual meeting of the American Society of Parasitologists, December 27-31, 1928, New York City. J. Parasitol. 15:135-149.

Cornwall, I. E.

1927. Some North Pacific whale barnacles. Contr. Canad. Biol. Toronto 23:501-517.

Cowles, R. P.

1908. Habits, reactions, and associations in *Ocypoda arenaria.* Pap. Tortugas Lab. Carnegie Inst. Wash. 2:1-41.

Crampton, H. E.

1917. Studies on the variation, distribution, and evolution of the genus Partula. Publ. Carnegie Inst. Washington 228:1-313.

1925. Contemporaneous organic differentiation in the species of Partula living in Moorea, Society Islands. Amer. Natur. 59:5-35.

Crane, Jocelyn

1947. Intertidal brachygnathous crabs from the west coast of tropical America with special reference to ecology. Zoologica 32:69-95.

Creaser, E. P.

1931. Some cohabitants of burrowing crayfish. Ecology 12:243-244.

Crile, G., Glasser, O., Telkes, M., and Rowland, A.

1932. Further studies of autosynthetic cells with special reference to the possible rôle of the nitro group in the energy phenomena of protoplasm. Proc. Amer. Phil. Soc. 71:411-420.

Crowder, W.

1931. Between the tides. N. Y. 1-461.

Crozier, W. G.

1929. On curves of growth, especially in relation to temperature. J. Gen. Physiol. 10:53-73.

Cunningham, J. T., & Reid, D. M.

1932. Experimental researches on the emission of oxygen by the pelvic filaments of the male Lepidosiren with some experiments on *Symbranchus marmoratus*. Proc. Roy. Soc. (B) 110:234-248.

Cunnington, W. A.

1920. The fauna of the African lakes: a study in comparative limnology with special reference to Tanganyika. Proc. Zool. Soc. London (1920):507-622.

Cushing, H., & Goetsch, E.

1915. Hibernation and the pituitary body. J. Exper. Med. 22:25-47.

Dachnowski, A. P., & Wells, B. W.

1929. The vegetation, stratigraphy, and age of the "open land" peat area in Carteret County, North Carolina. J. Washington Acad. Sci. 19:1-11.

Dahr, E.

1927. Studien über die Respiration der Landpulmonaten. Lunds. Univ. Arsskr. 23:1-120.

Dakin, W. J.

1912. Aquatic animals and their environment. The constitution of the external medium and its effect upon the blood. Internat. Rev. gesamt. Hydrobiol. und Hydrogr. 5:53-80.

1931. The composition of the blood of aquatic animals and its bearing upon the possible conditions of origin of the vertebrates. Nature (1931, 2):66-67.

Dakin, W. J., & C. M. G.

1925. The oxygen requirements of certain aquatic animals and its bearing upon the source of food supply. Brit. J. Exper. Biol. 2:293-322.

Damboviceanu, A. and Raplsine, L.

1925. Sur le pH interieur de certains éléments du liquide cavitaire chez *Sipunculus nudus*. C. R. Soc. Biol. Paris 93:1346.

Dammerman, K. W.

1926. The fauna of Durian and the Rio-Lingga Archipelago. Treubia 8:281-326.

1928. A comparison of the fauna of Krakatau with that of Christmas Island. Proc. 3 Pan-Pacific Congr. 1:966-972.

Darwin, C.

1875. On the origin of species by means of natural selection. 6 ed. New York xxi + 458.

Das, B. K.
1927. The bionomics of certain air-breathing fishes of India, together with an account of the development of their air-breathing organs. Phil. Tr. Roy. Soc. London B216:183-219.

Davenport, C. B.
1908. Experimental Morphology, xvii + 508.

Davies, W. M.
1928. The effect of variation in relative humidity on certain species of Collembola. British J. Exper. Biol. 6:79-86.

Davis, J. H.
1940. The ecology and geologic role of mangroves in Florida. Pap. Tortugas Lab. 32:303-412.

Davis, W. M.
1931. The origin of limestone caverns. Science 73:327-331.

Dekhuysen, C.
1921. Sur le semiperméabilité biologique de parios exterieures les Sipunculides. C. R. Acad. Sci. Paris 172:238-241.

Delaunay, M. H.
1924. Recherches biochimiques sur l'excretion azotee des invertebrés. Bull. Sta. Biol. Arcachon 21:41-84.

Dembowski, J. B.
1926. Notes on the behavior of the fiddler crab. Biol. Bull. 50:179-201.

Denis, W.
1922. The non-protein constituent in the blood of marine fish. J. Biol. Chem. 54:693-700.

Denny, F. E.
1927. Field method for determining the saltiness of brackish water. Ecology 8:106-112.

Derjavin, A. N.
1925. Materials of the Ponto-Azoph Carcinofauna. Russ. Hydrobiol. Zeitschr. 4:10-35.

Dexter, R. W.
1943. A suggested counting frame for intertidal population studies. Jour. Marine Res. 5:116-117.

Dhar, N. R.
1926. Influence of temperature on metabolism and the problem of acclimatization. Allahabad Univ. Stud. 2:313-328.

Dimon, A. C.
1905. The mud snail: *Nassa obsoleta.* Cold Spr. Harb. Monogr. 5:1-48.

Dole, R. B.
1914. Some chemical characteristics of sea-water at Tortugas, Florida. Pap. Tortugas Lab. Carnegie Inst. Washington 5:69-78.

Dolk, H. E., & Postma, N.
1927. Über die Haut- und die Lungenatmung von *Rana temporaria.* Zeitschr. vergl. Physiol. 5:417-444.

Donnan, F. G.
1929. The phenomena of life. Scientia 45:317-328.

Drew, G. H.
1914. On the precipitation of calcium carbonate in the sea by marine bacteria, and on the action of denitrifying bacteria in tropical and temperate seas. Pap. Tortugas Lab. Carnegie Inst. Washington 5:7-45.

Driesch, H.
1908. The science and philosophy of the organism. London, 2 vols. xiii + 329, xvi + 381.

Duryee, W. R.
1932. The relation between water content and oxygen consumption of certain freshwater organisms. Anat. Rec. 54:54.

Duval, Marcel
1924 Relation entre la concentration moleculaire du sang des crustaces et celle du milieu exterieur. C. R. Acad. Sci. Paris 178:1754-1757.
1927. Recherches sur le milieu interieur de *Telphusa fluviatilis* Latr. Adaptation de ce Crustacé d'eau douce aux changements de salinité. Bull. Inst. Oceanogr. Monaco (490):1-15.

Edge, E. R.
1934. Fecal pellets of some marine invertebrates. Amer. Midl. Nat. 15:78-84.

Edmonds, E.
1935. The relations between the internal fluid of marine invertebrates and the water of the environment with special reference to Australian Crustacea. Proc. Linn. Soc. N. S. Wales 60:233-247.

Eggert, B.
1929. Bestimmungstabelle und Beschreibung der Arten der Familie Periophthalmus. Zeitschr. f. Wiss. Zool. 133:398-410.
1929a. Die Gobienenflosse und ihre Anpassung an das Landleben. Zeitschr. wiss. Zool. 133:411-440.

Eichwald, P. E., & Fodor, P. A.
1919. Die Physikalisch-chemischen Grundlagen der Biologie. x + 510.

Eigenmann, C. H.
1898. The Origin of Cave Faunas. Proc. Ind. Acad. Sci. (1897):229-230.
1909. Cave vertebrates of America. Carnegie Inst. Washington, ix + 241.

Eisenbraut, M.
1932. Über die Wärmregulation beim Dreizehenfaudtier (*Bradypus tridactylus* L.). Zeitschr. wiss. Physiol. 16:39-47.

Ekman, S.
1920. Fortpflanzung und Lebenslauf der maringlazialen Relikte und ihrer marinen Stammformen. Internat. Rev. Hydrobiol. u. Hydrogr. 8:543-589.
1930. Die sudballischen maringlazialen Relikte und die Stauseetheorie. *Ibid.* 24:225-243.

Ellis, M. M., Merrick, A. D., & Ellis, M. D.
1930. The blood of North America freshwater mussels. Bull. U. S. Bur. Fisheries 46:509-542.

Elton, C.

1924. Periodic fluctuations in the numbers of animals: their causes and effects. Brit. J. Exper. Biol. 2:119-163.

1927. Animal ecology. New York, xx + 207.

Erdmann, Dr.

1896. Die Schlammhüpfer. Prometheus 7:730-732.

Evans, Gertrude

1939. Factors influencing the oxygen consumption of several species of plethodontid salamanders in aerial and aquatic media. Ecology 20:74-95.

Evans, R. G.

1947. The intertidal ecology of selected localities in the Plymouth neighborhood. J. Marine Biol. Assn. U. K. 27:173-218.

Faber, F. C.

1923. Zur Physiologie der Mangrove. Ber. d. Deutsch. Bot. Gesell. 41:227-234.

Fales, D. E.

1928. The light-receptive organs of certain barnacles. Biol. Bull. 54:534-547.

Fedele, M.

1927. Importanza dei fattori interni (fisiologici) nell distribuzione degli animali pelogici. Atti. Soc. Ital. Progr. Sci. (Roma) (1926):699-701.

Federighi, H.

1931. Salinity death-points of the oyster drill snail, *Urosalpinx cinerca* Say. Ecology 12:346-353.

Ferronniere, G.

1901. Etudes biologique sur les zones supralittorales de la Loire-Inférieure. Bull. Soc. Sci. nat. Ouest Nantes 11:1-451.

Findlay, A.

1913. Osmotic pressure. Monogr. Inorg. and Physical Chem. London, 1-84.

1914. Der osmotische Druck. Dresden u. Leipzig, viii + 96.

Finley, H. E.

1930. Toleration of freshwater Protozoa to increased salinity. Ecology 11:337-347.

Fischer, E.

1927. Sur la répartition des organismes qui pleuplent les rochers du littoral, un domaine exempt de vogues. Le role des courants. Bull. Soc. Zool. France 52:359-364.

1927b. Sur la limite supérieure de répartition de divers organismes en eau très calme. C. R. Acad. Sci. Paris 184:403-404.

1927c. Rapport entre le pouvoir réducteur de l'eau de mer et la repartition des organismes du littoral. *Ibid.* 185:1525-1527.

1928. De l'influence du phénomène des marées sur la répartition verticale des organismes littoraux. Bull. Soc. Zool. France 53:381-385.

Flattely, F. W.

1920. Rhythm in Nature. Sci. Progress 14:418-426.

1921. Some biological effects of the tides. *Ibid.* 16:251-257.

Flattely, F. W., & Walton, C. L.
1922. The biology of the seashore. New York, xvi + 336.
Fleure, H. J.
1907. On crabs which cling. Rep. Trans. Guernsey Soc. Nat. Sci. 5:177-184.
Florentin, R.
1899. Etudes sur la faune des mares salées de Lorraine. Ann. des Sci. Natur. (8) 10:209-346.
Forbes, H. O.
1885. A naturalist's wanderings in the Eastern Archipelago. London, xx + 536.
Forel, F. A.
1892-1904. Le Leman. Lausanne. 3 t.
Fowler, G. H. (E. J. Allen)
1928. The science of the sea. 2 ed. Oxford xxiii + 502.
Fowler, H. W.
1912. The Crustacea of New Jersey. Ann. Rept. N. J. State Mus. (1911):29-650.
Fox, H. M.
1929. Zoological results of the Cambridge expedition to the Suez Canal, 1924. Summary of results. Trans. Zool. Soc. London 22:843-863.
Fox, H. M., & Simmons, B. G.
1933. Metabolic rates of aquatic arthropods from different habitats. J. Exper. Biol. 10:67-74.
Fraenkel, G.
1927. Beitrage zur Geotaxis und Phototaxis von Littorina. Zeitschr. vergl. Physiol. 5:585-597.
Fredericq, L.
1922. Action du milieu marin sur les animaux Invertébrés. Bull. Acad. Roy. Bruxelles (5) 8:423-426.
Fraser, J. H.
1932. Observations on the fauna and constituents of an estuarine mud in a polluted area. J. Marine Biol. Assn. U. K. 18:69-85.
Fry, F. E. J.
1937. The summer migration of the cisco, *Leucichthys artedi,* in Lake Nipissing, Ontario. Univ. Toronto Stud. Biol. 44:1-91.
Fulton, B. B.
1933. Inheritance of song in hybrids of two subspecies of *Nemobius fasciatus* (Orthoptera). Ann. Entomol. Soc. Amer. 26:368-376.
Fulton, J. F.
1921. Concerning the vitality of *Actinia bermudensis:* a study in symbiosis. J. Exper. Zool. 33:353-364.
Gage, S. H.
1892. The comparative physiology of respiration. Amer. Nat. 26:817-832.
Gail, F. W.
1920. Some experiments with Fucus to determine the factors controlling its vertical distribution. Puget Sound Mar. Biol. Sta Publ. 2:139-151.

1920a. Hydrogen ion concentration and other factors affecting the distribution of Fucus. *Ibid.* 2:287-306.

Galloway, T. McL.

1933. The osmotic pressure and saline content of the blood of *Petromyzon fluviatilis.* J. Exper. Biol. 10:313-316.

Gardiner, J. S.

1903. The fauna and geography of the Maldive and Laccadive Archipelagoes. Cambridge 1:ix + 470; 2:viii + 1040.

Garrey, W. E.

1905. The osmotic pressure of sea water and of the blood of marine animals. Biol. Bull. 8:257-270.

1915. Some cryoscopic and osmotic data. *Ibid.* 28:77-86.

1916. The resistance of freshwater fish to changes of osmotic and chemical conditions. Am. J. Physiol. 39:313-329.

Garstang, W.

1905. Respiration in sand-burrowing crabs. Trans. Norfolk and Norwich Nat. Hist. Soc. 8:22-24.

Gaschott, O.

1927. Die Mollusken des Littorals der Alpen- und Voralpenseen im Gebiete der Ostalpen. Internat. Rev. ges. Hydrodiol. u. Hydrogr. 17:304-335.

Gates, R. R.

1927. A botanist in the Amazon Valley. An account of the flora and fauna in the land of floods. London, 1-203.

Gauthier, H.

1927. Sur la présence de la *Caridina togoensis* Kingsl. f. *stuhlmanni* Hilg. (Décapodes, *Caridea*) dans le Tassili des Ajjers (Sahara central). Bull. Soc. Hist. Nat. Afrique du Nord 18:127-131.

1928. Recherches sur la faune des eaux continentales de l'Algerie et Tunisie Alger. 1-420.

Germain, L.

1913. Origine de la fauna fluviatile d'Est Africain. 9e Congr. intern. Zool. Monaco (1914):559-571.

Gersbacher, W. M., & Denison, M.

1930. Experiments with animals in tide pools. Publ. Puget Sound Biol. Sta. 7:209-215.

Gessner, F.

1931. Ökologische Untersuchungen an Salzwiesen. I. Salz- und Wassergehalt des Bodens als Standortsfaktoren. Ihre Abhängigkeit vom Gefälle. Mitt. naturw. Ver. Neuvorpommern 57/58:53-78.

Gislen, Torsten

1947. Conquering terra firma. The transition from water to land life. Kerngl. Fisiographliska Sallskapets I Lund Forhandlingar 17:1-20.

Gjaja, I.

1922. Sur la consommation d'oxygéne des animaux marin lorsqu'ils se trouvent dans l'air atmosphérique, Ghlas. Srpska Akad. Belgrade 105:35-41.

Gompel, M., & Legendre, R.
1927. Effects de la temperature, de la salure, et du pH sur les larves de homards. Compt. Rend. Soc. Biol. 97:1058-1060.

Goodhart, C. B.
1941. The ecology of the Amphipoda in a small estuary in Hampshire. J. Animal Ecol. 10:306-322.

Goodrich, E. S.
1924. Living organisms. An account of their origin and evolution. Oxford, 1-200.
1930. Studies on the structure and development of vertebrates. London, xiii + 837.

Gortner, R. A.
1933. The water content of medusae. Science 77:282-283.

Graham, R. M.
1931. Notes on the mangrove swamps of Kenya. J. East Africa and Uganda Nat. Hist. Soc. 36:157-164.

Gray, J.
1926. The growth of fish. I. The relationship between embryo and yolk in *Salmo fario*. Brit. J. Exper. Biol. 4:215-225.
1928. The rôle of water in the evolution of terrestrial vertebrates. *Ibid.* 6:26-31.

Greene, C. W.
1905. Physiological studies of the Chinook salmon. Bull. U. S. Bu. Fisheries 24:431-456.

Gregory, J. W.
1931. Raised beaches and variations of sea-level. Scientia 49:95-104.

Gregory, W. K.
1933. The new anthropogeny—twenty-five stages of vertebrate evolution, from Silurian chordate to man. Science 77:29-40.

Gross, P. M.
1933. The "salting out" of non-electrolytes from aqueous solutions. Chem. Rev. 13:91-100.

Gulick, A.
1932. Biological peculiarities of oceanic islands. Q. Rev. Biol. 7:405-427.
1948. The evolution of terrestrial life as seen by a biochemist. Sci. Mo. 67:267-272.

Gunter, G.
1942. A list of fishes of the mainland of North America and Middle America recorded from both freshwater and sea water. Amer. Midl. Nat. 28:305-326.
1947. Paleoecological import of certain relationships of marine animals to salinity. J. Paleontol. 21:77-79.

Gurley, S.
1909. Migrations by intoxications. Am. J. Psychol. 20:102-108.

Gurney, R.
1923. A sea-anemone (*Sagartia luciae* Verrill) in brackish water in Norfolk. Trans. Norfolk and Norwich Nat. Soc. 11:434-437.

Haan, J. de and Bakker, A.
1924. Renal function in summer frogs and winter frogs. J. Physiol. Cambr. 59:129-137.

Hall, F. G.
1922. The vital limit of exsiccation of certain animals. Biol. Bull. 41:31-51.
1924. The functions of the swimbladder of fishes. *Ibid.* 47:79-127.
1929. The ability of marine fishes to remove dissolved oxygen. Anat. Rec. 44:197.

Hall, T. S.
1901. A burrowing fish (*Galaxias* sp.) Victorian Nat. 18:65-66.

Hall, V. E.
1931. The muscular activity and oxygen consumption of *Urechis caupo.* Biol. Bull. 61:400-416.

Hamburger, R.
1904. Ueber die paarigen Extremitäten von Squalius, Trigla, Periophthalmus und Lophius. Rev. Suisse Zool. 12:71-148.

Hamilton, C. C.
1917. The behavior of some soil insects in a gradient of evaporating power of air, carbon dioxide, and ammonia. Biol. Bull. 32:159-182.

Hardy, A. C.
1944. Explanation, a non-technical account of the contents of the volume for the general reader, intended to show the bearing of the work upon the future welfare of the fishing industry. Hiell Bull. Marine Ecol. Suppl. 1: i — xcii. B. A. 19:1687.

Harms, W.
1914. Über die Augen der am Grunde der Gewässerlebenden Fische. Zool. Anz. 44:35-42.
1929. Die Realisation von Genen und die consekutive Adaption. I. Phasen in der Differenzierung der Anlagenkomplexe und die Frage Landtierwerdung. Zeitschr. wiss. Zool. 133:211-397.
1932. Die Realisation von Genen und die konsecutive Adaptation. II. *Birgus latro* Linné als Landkrebs und seine Beziehungen zu den Coenobiten. *Ibid.* 140:167-290.

Harms, J. W., & Dragendorff, O.
1933. Osmotische Untersuchungen an *Physcosoma lurco Sel.* und de Man aus den Mangrove-Vorländern der Sunda-Inseln. Zeitschr. wiss. Zool. A143: 263-323.

Harvey, E. N.
1914. The relation between the rate of penetration of marine tissues by alkali and the change in functional activity induced by the alkali. Pap. Tortugas Lab. Carnegie Inst. Washington 6:131-146.

Harvey, H. W.
1928. Biological chemistry and physics of sea water. Cambridge, x + 194.

Hatch, M. H.
1946. Beetles. The Biologist 28:66-80.

Hathaway, E. S.

1927. The relation of temperature to the quantity of food consumed by fishes. Ecology 8:428-434.

1928. Quantitative study of the changes produced by acclimatization in the tolerance of high temperatures by fishes and amphibians. Bull. U. S. Bur. Fish. 43:169-192.

Havinga, B.

1930. Der Granat (*Crangon vulgaris* Fabr.) in den holländischen Gewässern. Cons. Perm. Internat. Explor. Mer. J. Conseil. 5:57-87.

Hawthorne, W. C.

1930. Diffusion, osmosis, and osmotic pressure. Sci. Mo. 31:535-542.

Hay, W. P., & Shore, C. A.

1918. The decapod crustaceans of Beaufort, N. C., and the surrounding region. Bull. U. S. Bu. Fisheries 35:371-475.

Hayes, F. R.

1927. Effect of environmental factors on the development and growth of *Litorina littorea.* Proc. and Trans. Nova Scotian Inst. Sci. 17:6-13.

1927a. The negative geotropism of the periwinkle: a study in littoral ecology. *Ibid.* 16:155-173.

1930. The physiological response of Paramaecium in sea water. Physiol. Zool 4:409-422.

Heape, W.

1931. Emigration, migration, and nomadism. Cambridge xii + 369.

Hedgpeth, J. W.

1949. The North American species of Macrobrachium. Texas Jour. Sci. 1:28-38

Helff, O. M.

1931. The effect of lung extirpation on life, oxygen consumption, and metamorphosis of *Rana pipiens* larvae. J. Exper. Zool. 59:167-178.

Helff, O. M., & Stubblefield, K. I.

1929. Influence of decreasing oxygen tensions on the respiration of *Rana pipiens* larvae. Anat. Rec. 44:216-217.

Helland-Hansen, B.

1912. The ocean waters, an introduction to physical oceanography. Internat Rev. ges. Hydrobiol. u. Hydrog.

1923. Suppl. 11:1-84; 393-496.

Hendee, Esther C.

1933. The association of termites with fungi. Science 77:212-213.

Henninger, G.

1907. Die Labyrinthorgane bei Labyrinthfischen. Zool. Jahrb. Anat. 25:251-304.

Herre, A. W.

1927. Gobies of the Philippines and the China Sea. Monogr. Bur. Sci. Philippine Isl. 23:1-352.

1928. Philippine gobies. Proc. 3 Pan-Pacific Congr. Tokyo 2:2257-2266.

Hess, C.

1913. Gesichtssinn. Winterstein's Handb. vergl. Physiol. 4:555-840.

Hesse, R.
1920. Die Anpassung der Meerestiere an das Leben im Süsswasser. Bonn, 1-6.

Hetherington, A.
1932. Is the usual balanced physiological medium suitable for avascular freshwater animals? Anat. Rec. 54:40-41.

Hewatt, W. G.
1937. Ecological studies on selected marine intertidal communities of Monterey Bay, California. Amer. Midl. Nat. *18:*161-206.

Hewitt, C. G.
1907. Ligia. Liverpool M. B. C. Mem.

Hill, A. V.
1931. Adventures in biophysics. Philadelphia, ix + 162.

Hinman, E. H.
1932. The utilization of water colloids and material in solution by aquatic animals with especial reference to mosquito larvae. Q. Rev. Biol. 7:210-217.

Hogben, L. T.
1926. Comparative physiology. New York, xiv + 219.

Hogben, E., & Zoond, A.
1930. Respiratory exchange in the freshwater crab, *Potamoneustes perlatus.* T. Roy. Soc. South Africa 18:283-286.

Holl, F. G.
1932. The ecology of certain fishes and amphibians with special reference to their helminth and linguatulid parasites. Ecol. Monogr. 2:83-107.

Hopkins, F. G.
1933. Some chemical aspects of life. Science 78:219-231.

Hora, S. L.
1930. Ecology, bionomics, and evolution of the torrential fauna, with special reference to the organs of attachment. Philosoph. T. Roy. Soc. London (B) 218:171-282.
1930a. The value of field observations in the study of organic evolution. J. Bombay Nat. Hist. Soc. 34:374-385.
1933. Respiration in fishes. *Ibid.* 36:538-560.
1935. Modification of swimbladder in certain air-breathing fishes of India. Current Sci. 3:336-338.

Hori, J.
1928. On the relation between the temperature and vitality of the oyster preserved in air. J. Imper. Fish. Inst. Tôkyô 23:127-130.

Hornaday, W. T.
1885. Two years in the jungle. New York, xxii + 512.

Horst, R.
1902. On the habits of the cocoanut crab or palm thief (*Birgus latro* Fabr.). Notes Leyden Mus. 23:143-146.

Hoy, P. R.
1873. Deep-water fauna of Lake Michigan. Ann. Mag. Nat. Hist. (4) 11:319-320.

Hubbard, G. D., & Wilder, C. G.
1930. Validity of the indicators of ancient climates. Bull. Geol. Soc. Amer. 41:275-292.

Hubbs, C. L.
1928. An hypothesis on the origin of graded series of local races in fishes. Anat. Rec. 41:49.
1940. Speciation of fishes. Amer. Midl. Nat. 74:198-211.

Hukuda, K.
1932. Change of weight of marine animals in diluted media. J. Exper. Biol. 9:61-68.

Hungerford, H. B.
1919. The biology and ecology of aquatic and semi-aquatic Hemiptera. Kansas Univ. Sci. Bull. 11:3-341.

Huntington, E.
1927. The character of races as influenced by physical environment, natural selection and historical development. New York, xvii + 393.

Huntsman, A. G.
1918. Fisheries research in the Gulf of St. Lawrence in 1917. Canadian Fisherman (May):1-5.
1918a. The vertical distribution of certain intertidal animals. Proc. Roy. Soc. Canada 11:53-60.
1918b. The effect of the tide on the distribution of the fishes of the Canadian Atlantic Coast. Proc. Roy. Soc. Canada 12:61-67.
1920. Climates of our Atlantic waters. Amer. Fish. Soc. 50:326-333.
1924. Limiting factors for marine animals. I. The lethal effect of sunlight. Contrib. Canadian Biol. 2:83-88.
1924a. II. Resistance of larval lobsters to extreme temperatures. *Ibid.* 2:91-92.

Huntsman, A. G., & Sparks, M. I.
1924b. Relative resistance to high temperatures. *Ibid.* 2:97-114.

Hutchinson, G. Evelyn
1931. On the occurrence of Trichocorixa Kirkaldy (Corixidae, Hemiptera-Heteroptera) in salt water and its zoo-geographical significance. Amer. Nat. 65:573-574.

Hyman, O. W.
1920. The development of Gelasimus after hatching. J. Morphol. 33:485-501.
1922. Adventures in the life of a fiddler crab. Smithsonian R. (1920):443-460.

Jacobs, M. H.
1919. Acclimatization as a factor affecting the upper thermal death points of organisms. J. Exper. Zool. 27:427-442.
1933. The relation between cell volume and penetration from an isosmotic solution. J. Cell. Comp. Physiol. 3:29-43.

Jehu, T. J.
1923. The origin of terrestrial vertebrates. T. Edinb. Geol. Soc. 11:251-252.

Jenkins, J. T.
1935. A textbook of oceanography. N. Y. x + 206.

Jewell, M. E., & Broun, H. W.
1929. Studies on Northern Michigan bog lakes. Ecology 10:427-475.
Joad, C. E. M.
1928. The future of man. Harper's Mo. Mag. (1928) 57:492-500.
Johansen, A. C.
1918. Randers Fjords' Naturhistorie. Koebenhavn, iii + 500.
Johnson, D. S., & York, H. H.
1915. The relation of plants to tide levels. Carnegie Inst. Wash. Publ. 206:1-162.
Johnson, D. S., & Skutch, A. F.
1928. Littoral vegetation on a headland of Mt. Desert Island, Maine. I. Submersible or strictly littoral vegetation. Ecology 9:188-215.
Johnson, J.
1928. Constant temperature and humidity chambers. Phytopath. 18:227-238.
Johnstone, J.
1908. Conditions of life in the sea. Cambridge, vii + 329.
Jordan, D. S.
1905. The origin of species through isolation. Science 22:545-562.
Jordan, H. J.
1930. La réglage de la consommation de l'orygène chez les animaux à "tension gazeuse alveolaire inconstante" Arch. Néerland. Phys. Homme et Animaux (3C) 15:198-212.
Joubin, L.
1928. Eléments de biologie marine. Paris, 1-355.
Just, E. E.
1930. The fertilization capacity of Nereis after exposure to hypotonic sea-water. Protoplasma 10:24-32.
1930a. Fertilization and development of Nereis eggs in dilute sea-water. *Ibid.* 10:33-40.
Karsten, H.
1923. Das Auge von *Periophthalmus koelreuteri.* Jenaische Zeitschr. f. Naturwiss. 59:115-154.
Keilin, D.
1921. On some dipterous larvae infesting the branchial chambers of landcrabs. Ann. Mag. Nat. Hist. (9) 8:601-608.
Kennedy, C. H.
1917. Some factors involved in the resting habit of birds. Condor 19:87-93.
1925. The distribution of certain insects of reversed behavior. Biol. Bull. 48: 390-401.
1927. The exoskeleton as a factor in limiting and directing the evolution of insects. J. Morphol. and Physiol. 44:267-312.
1927a. Some non-nervous factors that condition the sensivity of insects to moisture, temperature, light, and odors. Ann. Entomol. Soc. Amer. 20: 87-106.
1928. Evolutionary level in relation to geographic, seasonal and diurnal distribution of insects. Ecology 9:367-379.

Kenyon, A.
1925. Digestive enzymes in poikilothermal vertebrates. Bull. U. S. Bur. Fisheries 41:181-200.

Keys, A.
1933. The mechanism of adaptation to varying salinity in the common eel and the general problem of osmotic regulation in fishes. P. Roy. Soc. B112: 185-197.

Keys, A., & Bateman, J. B.
1932. Branchial responses to adrenaline and to pitressin in the eel. Biol. Bull. 63:327-336.

Keys, A., & Willmer, E. N.
1932. "Chloride secreting cells" in the gills of fishes, with special reference to the common eel. J. Physiol. 76:368-378.

Keys, A. B.
1931. A study of the selective action of decreased salinity and of asphyxiation on the Pacific killifish, *Fundulus parvipinnis*. Bull. Scripps Inst. Oceanogr. 2:417-490.

King, L. A. L.
1914. Notes on the habits and characteristics of some littoral mites of Millport. Proc. Roy. Phys. Soc. Edinb. 19:129-141.
1914a. Marine Biological Association of the West of Scotland. Annual Rept. 1913, 1-125.

King, L. A. L., & Russell, E. S.
1909. A method for the study of the animal ecology of the shore. Roy. Phys. Soc. Edinburgh 17:225-253.

Kirby, H.
1932. Two Protozoa from brine. Trans. Amer. Microscop. Soc. 51:8-15.
1932a. Some salt marsh ciliates in California. Anat. Rec. 54:100.

Klugh, A. B.
1921. A correction concerning the life zones of Canada. Biol. Bull. 41:272-275.
1925. Ecological photometry and a new instrument for measuring light. Ecology 6:203.
1927. A comparison of certain methods of measuring light for ecological purposes. *Ibid.* 8:415-427.

Knudsen, M.
1901. Hydrographical tables. Copenhagen and London. v + 63.

Koidsumi, H.
1928. On the fatal effect of sea water upon the larvae of *Chironomus viridicollis*. Dob. Z. 40:131-142.

Koidsumi, K.
1931. On the toxic action of sea-water on a freshwater insect larva (*Chironomus viridicollis* (Van der Wulp). J. Soc. Trop. Agr. 3:248-263.

Kokubo, S.
1930. Contribution to the research on the respiration of fishes. II. Studies on the acidosis of fishes. Sci. Rept. Tôhoku Imp. Univ. Biol. (4)5:249-390.

Kraft, C. F.

1931. Can science explain life? Lancaster, Pa., 1-98.

Krogh, A.

1904. On the cutaneous and pulmonary respiration of the frog. Skand. Arch. Physiol. 15:328-419.

1916. The respiratory exchange of animals and man. (Monogr. on Biochem.). London, viii + 173.

1931. Dissolved substances as food for aquatic organisms. Biol. Rev. 6:412-442.

Krümmel, O.

1907, 1911. Handbuch der Oceanographie. Stuttgart 2 vols. vii + 526, xvi + 766.

Kuhn,

1927. Farbensinn der Tiere. Tabulae Biologicae 4:376-378.

Kühnholtz-Lordat, G.

1926. Un cas de zonation dans sables maritimes. Feuille Nat. 47:138-139.

1926a. Une succession dans les vases salées de l'embouchure de la Seudre (Charente-Inférieure). *Ibid.* 47:145-150.

Kuamoto, A.

1914. Chinzai-Ihô No. 155 May.

Labbé, A.

1922. La distribution des animaux des marais salants dans ses rapports avec la concentration en ions hydrogène. C. R. Acad. Sci. Paris 175:913-915.

1926. L'origine des marais salants du Croisic. Ann. Inst. Oceanogr. 3:335-369.

La Face, Lidia

1928. Sulla resistenza della larve degli anofilini alla salinita. Riv. Malariologia 7:18-30.

Lameere, A.

1917. L'evolution des premiers organismes. Ann. Soc. Zool. Malac. Bruxelles 51:11-46.

Lang, A. (Bernard)

1891. Textbook of comparative anatomy. Pt. 1, London, xviii + 562.

de Laubenfels, M. W.

1947. Ecology of the sponges of a brackish water environment, at Beaufort, N. C. Ecol. Monogr. 17:31-46.

Laurens, H.

1928. The physiological effects of radiation. Physiol. Rev. 8:1-91.

Lengersdorf, F.

1929. Beiträge zur Kenntnis der Höhlenfauna Westfalens. Verhandl. Naturhist. Ver. Preuss. Reinlande u. Westfalens 85:106-108.

Lieber, Alice

1931. Experimentell-biologische Untersuchungen in der Verlandungszone des Federsees. Zool. Anzeig. 96:209-239.

Lindeman, V. F.

1928. The physiology of the crustacean heart. I. The effect of various ions upon the heart rhythm of the crayfish, *Cambarus clarkii*. Physiol. Zool. 1:576-592.

1929. II. The effect of lithium, ammonium, strontium, and barium ions upon the heart rhythm of the crayfish, *Cambarus clarkii*. *Ibid.* 2:395-410.

Lipman, C. B.

1924. A critical and experimental study of Drew's bacterial hypothesis on $CaCO_3$ precipitation in the sea. Pap. Dept. Marine Biol. Carnegie Inst. Washington 19:181-191.

1929. Further studies on marine bacteria with special reference to the Drew hypothesis on $CaCO_3$ precipitation in the sea. *Ibid.* 26:231-248.

1929a. The chemical composition of sea water. *Ibid.* 26:249-257.

Lite, J. C., & Whitney, D. D.

1925. The rôle of aeration in the hatching of fertilized eggs of rotifers. J. Exper. Zool. 43:1-9.

Littleford, R. A., Keller, W. F., & Phillips, N. E.

1947. Studies on the vital limits of water loss in plethodont salamanders. Ecology 28:440-447.

Loeb, J.

1903. On the relative toxicity of distilled water, sugar solutions, and solutions of the various constituents of the sea water for marine animals. Univ. Cal. Publ. Physiol. 1:55-69.

1916. The mechanism of the diffusion of electrolytes through the membranes of living cells. J. Biol. Chem. 27:339-375.

Ludwig, D.

1945. The effects of atmospheric humidity on animal life. Physiol. Zool. 18: 103-135.

Lull, R. S.

1917. Organic evolution. New York, xviii + 729.

1929. Organic evolution. Rev. ed. N. Y. xix + 743.

Lusk, G.

1917. The elements of the science of nutrition. 3 ed., Philadelphia, 1-841.

Lutz, Bertha

1948. Ontogenetic evolution in frogs. Evolution 2:29-39.

Lyon, F. L., & Buckman, H. O.

1922. The nature and properties of soils. New York, 1-588.

Macallum, A. B.

1904. The palaeochemistry of the ocean. Trans. Canadian Inst. 7:535-562.

MacArthur, J. W., & Baillie, W. H. T.

1929. Metabolic activity and duration of life. J. Exper. Zool. 53:221-268.

Macfarlane, J. M.

1918. The causes and course of organic evolution: a study in bioenergics. N. Y. ix + 875.

MacGinitie, G. E.

1935. Ecological aspects of a California marine estuary. Amer. Midl. Nat. 16:629-765.

Marcus, K.

1911. Über Geruchsorgane bei decapoden Krebsen aus der Gruppe der Galatheiden. Zeitschr. Wiss. Zool. 79:511-545.

Margaria, R.

1931. The osmotic changes in some marine animals. P. Roy. Soc. London B107: 606-624.

Marmer, H. A.

1930. The sea. N. Y. xi + 312.

1944. The vertical stability of the coast at Boston in the light of recent tide observations. J. Marine Res. 5:206-213.

Marshall, E. K., & Smith, H. W.

1930. The glomerular development of the vertebrate kidney in relation to habitat. Biol. Bull. 59:135-153.

Marukawa, H., & Kamiya, T.

1930. Some results of the migration of important food fish. Jour. Imp. Fisheries Exper. Sta. Tokyo 1:1-38.

Matheson, R., & Hinman, E. H.

1930. A seasonal study of the plancton of a spring fed Chara pool versus that of a temporary to semitranspermanent woodland pool in relation to mosquito breeding. Amer. J. Hygiene 11:174-188.

Matthes, E.

1927. Der Einfluss des Mediumwechsels auf das Geruchsvermögen von Triton. Zeitschr. vergl. Physiol. 5:83-166.

Mayer, A. G.

1914. The effects of temperautre upon tropical marine animals. Pap. Tortugas Lab. Carnegie Inst. Washington 6:1-24.

1918. Toxic effects due to high temperature. *Ibid.* 12:173-178.

1922. Hydrogen-ion concentration and electrical conductivity of the surface water of the Atlantic and Pacific. *Ibid.* 18:61-65.

McClendon, J. F.

1917. The standardization of a new colorometric method for the determination of the hydrogen-ion concentration, CO_2 tension, and CO_2 and O_2 content of sea water, of animal heat, and of CO_2 of the air, with a summary of similar data on bicarbonate solutions in general. J. Biol. Chem. 30:265-288, 459.

1918. On changes in the sea and their relation to organisms. Pap. Dept. Mar. Biol. Carnegie Inst. Washington 12:213-259.

McCrea, R. H.

1926. The salt marsh vegetation of Little Island, Co. Cork. J. Ecol. 14:342-346.

McDougall, K. D.

1943. Sessile marine invertebrates at Beaufort, North Carolina. Ecol. Monogr. 13:321-374.

Medwedewa, N. B.

1927. Über den osmotischen Druck der Hämolymphe von *Artemia salina.* Zeitschr. vergl. Physiol. 5:547-554.

Meek, A.
1913. The migration of crabs. Rept. Dove Marine Lab. Cullercoats 2:13-20, 3:73-76.

Mekeel, A. G.
1930. The heart of the lungless salamander. Anat. Rec. 47:354.

Mellanby, K.
1932. The influence of atmospheric humidity on the thermal death point of a number of insects. J. Exper. Biol. 9:222-231.

Metcalf, M. M.
1929. Parasites and the aid they give in problems of taxonomy, geographical distribution, and paleogeography. Smithsonian Misc. Coll. 81 (8) :1-36.
1930. Salinity and size. Science 72:526-527.

Metcalf, Z. P.
1924. The beach pool leaf hopper complex. Ecology 5:171-174.

Miles, W. H.
1920. Experiments on the behavior of some Puget Sound shore fishes (Blenniidae). Publ. Puget Sound Biol. Sta. 2:79-94.

Miller, R. C., Ramage, W. D., & Lazier, E. L
1928. A study of physical and chemical conditions in San Francisco Bay, especially in relation to the tides. Univ. California Publ. Zool. 31:201-267.

Miner, R. W.
1912. The sea worm group. Amer. Mus. Nat. Hist. Jour. 12:244-250.

Miura, T.
1929. Distribution of benthonic organisms and hardness of sea-bottom. J. Imp. Fisheries Inst. Tokyo 25:15-20.

Moberg, E. G.
1927. Effect of tidal changes on physical, chemical, and biological conditions in the sea water of the San Diego region. I. Observations on the effect of tidal changes on physical and chemical conditions of sea water in the San Diego region. Bull. Scripps Inst. Oceanogr. Tech. Ser. 1:1-14.

Moltoni, E.
1927. Esperienze sulle condizioni di vita delle larve di alcune zangare nell posse d'acqua salata nei dintorni di Cagliari. Natura 18:28-37.

Monterosso, B.
1927. Studi cirripedologici I, Anidrobiosi, "clidotropismo," e allevamente di *Chthamalus stellatus* Ranzani. Atti Accad. Gioenia Sci. Nat. Catania 15:1-20.
1929. Studii cirripedologici. V. Anabiosi e revwescenza nei Ctamalini. Atti R. Accad. Naz. Lincei. Rend. cl. Sci. Fis. Mat. e Nat. 9:92-96.

Montfort, C.
1926. Physiologische und pflanzengeographische Seesalzwirkungen. I. Einfluss ausgeglichener Salzlösungen auf Mesophyll- und Schliesszellen; Kritik der Iljinschen Hypothese der Salzbeständigkeit. Jarb. wiss. Bot. 65:502-550.

Moore, B.
1913. The origin and nature of life. New York, 1-256.

Moore, B., Edie, E. S., Whitney, E., & Dakin, W. J.
1912. Nutrition and metabolism of marine animals in relationship to (a) dissolved organic matter and (b) particulate organic matter of sea water. Biochem. J. 6:255-296.

Moore, J. E. S.
1903. The Tanganyika problem. London.

Morgan, Ann H., & Grierson, M. C.
1932. The functions of the gills in burrowing mayflies (*Hexagenia recurvata*). Physiol. Zool. 5:230-244.

Morgan, Ann H., & O'Neil, H. D.
1931. The functions of the tracheal gills in the larvae of the caddis fly, *Macronema zebratum* Hagen. Physiol. Zool. 4:361-378.

Morgan, A. H., & Porter, M.
1929. The effect of removing tracheal gills from mayfly nymphs. Anat. Rec 44:221-222.

Morgan, Ann H., & Sondheim, S. C.
1932. Attempts to reduce the gills in neotenous newts, *Triturus viridescens* Anat. Rec. 52:7-29.

Morris, C.
1892. The origin of lungs. Amer. Nat. 26:975-986.

Muenscher, W. L. C.
1915. Ability of seaweeds to withstand desiccation. Pudget Sound Mar. Sta. Publ. 1:19-23.

Murray, J.
1895. Editorial notes. Rept. Sci. Results Challenger Exped. 1:vii-xxxii, xxxii-liii, 1-796, 797-1608.

Murray, J., & Hjort, J.
1912. The depths of the ocean. London, xx + 821.

Muttkowski, R. A.
1918. The fauna of Lake Mendota. A qualitative and quantitative survey with special reference to the insects. Wis. Acad. Sci., Arts, Lett. 19:374-482.

Nash, J.
1931. The number and size of glomeruli in the kidneys of fishes, with observations on the morphology of the renal tubules of fishes. Am. J. Anat. 47: 425-446.

Needham, J.
1930. On the penetration of marine organisms into freshwater. Biol. Zentralb. 50:504-509.

Needham, J. G., & Heywood, H. B.
1929. A handbook of the dragonflies of North America. Springfield, Ill., viii + 378.

Nelson, T. C.
1928. Relation of spawning of the oyster to temperature. Ecology 9:145-154.

Newbegin, M. I.
1931. Life by the seashore. London, 1-296.

Nicol, Edith A. T.
1935. The ecology of a salt-marsh. J. Mar. Biol. Assn. Unit. Kgd. 20:203-262.

Nikitinsky, J.
1928. Über die Wirkung der Kohlensäure auf Wasserorganismen. Centralb. Bakt. 73:481-483.

Noble, G. K.
1925. The integumentary, pulmonary, and cardiac modifications correlated with increased cutaneous respiration in the Amphibia: a solution of the "Hairy Frog" problem. J. Morphol. 40:341-416.
1927. The plethodontid salamanders; some aspects of their evolution. Amer. Mus. Nov. (249):1-26.
1929. Further observations on the life-history of the newt, *Triturus viridescens*. *Ibid.* (348):1-21.
1929a. The adaptive modifications of the arboreal tadpoles of Hoplophryne and the torrent tadpoles of Staurois. Bull. Amer. Mus. Nat. Hist. 58:291-334.
1931. The biology of the Amphibia. New York, xii + 577.

Noble, G. K., & Brady, M. K.
1933. Observations on the life history of the marbled salamander, *Ambystoma opacum* Gravenhorst. Zoologica 11:89-132.

Noland, L. E.
1925. Factors influencing the distribution of freshwater ciliates. Ecology 6:437-452.

Numanoi, H.
1934. Relation between atmospheric humidity and evaporation of water in *Ligia exotica*. J. Facul. Sci. Imp. Univ. Tokyo (4)3:343-350.

Nuttall, G. H. F.
1911. On the adaptations of ticks to the habits of their hosts. Parasitol. 4:46-67.

Oka, A.
1922. Vertrocknung und Wiederbelebung bei einer Süsswasser-Hirudenee. Zool. Anz. 54:92-94.

Olsen, J. C.
1916. A text-book of quantitative chemical analysis by gravimetric, electrolytic, volumetric, and gasometric methods. New York, xxi + 555.

Osborn, H. F.
1917. The origin and evolution of life. New York, xxi + 332.
1925. The origin of species as revealed by vertebrate paleontology. Nature 115: 925-926, 961-963.
1933. Recent revivals of Darwinism. Science 77:199-202.

Osburn, R. C.
1914. Bryozoa of the Tortugas Islands, Florida. Pap. Tortugas Lab., Carnegie Inst. 5:181-222.

Packard, E. L.
1918. A quantitative analysis of the molluscan fauna of San Francisco Bay. U. of Cal. Publ. Zool. 18:299-336.

Page, I. H.

1927. The composition of Woods Hole sea water. Biol. Bull. 52:147-160.

Pantin, C. F. A.

1931. The origin of the composition of the body fluids in animals. Biol. Rev. and Biol. Proc. Cambridge Philos. Soc. 6:459-482.

Pearse, A. S.

1911. Concerning the development of frog tadpoles in sea water. Philippine J. Sci. (D) 6:219-220.

1914. Observations on the fauna of the rock beaches at Nahant, Massachusetts. Bull. Wis. Nat. Hist. Soc. 11:8-34; 12:72-80.

1914a. Habits of fiddler crabs. Smithsonian Rept. (1913):415-428.

1915. An account of the Crustacea collected by the Walker Expedition to Santa Marta, Colombia. Proc. U. S. Nat. Mus. 49:531-556.

1918. The food of the shore fishes of certain Wisconsin lakes. Bull. U. S. Bu. Fisheries 35:245-292.

1922. The effects of environment on animals. Amer. Nat. 56:144-158.

1926. Animal Ecology. New York, ix + 417.

1926a. Success. Sci. Mo. 23:46-49.

1927. The migration of animals from the ocean into freshwater and land habitats. Amer. Nat. 61:466-479.

1928. On the ability of certain marine invertebrates to live in diluted sea water. Biol. Bull. 54:405-409.

1928a. The gobies of the Gulf of Guinea. Sci. Mo. 27:239-243.

1929. Observations on certain littoral and terrestrial animals at Tortugas, Florida, with special reference to migrations from marine to terrestrial habitats. Pap. Tortugas Sta. Carnegie Inst. Washington 391:205-223.

1929a. The ecology of certain estuarine crabs at Beaufort, N. C. J. Elisha Mitch. Soc. 44:230-237.

1930. Ecology of certain Oriental land fishes and crustaceans. Anat. Rec. 47:355.

1930a. Parasites of Fukien crabs. Proc. Nat. Hist. Soc. Fukien Christ. Univ. 3:1-9.

1930b. Parasites of Japanese Crustacea. Ann. Zool. Japan 13:1-8.

1931. The ecology of certain crustaceans on the beaches at Misaki, Japan, with special reference to migrations from sea to land. J. Elisha Mitch. Sci. Soc. 46:161-166.

1931a. The beaches at Misaki. J. Pan. Pacific Res. Inst. 6:3-6.

1932. Environment and heredity. Sci. Mo. 34:541-544.

1932a. Observations on the ecology of certain fishes and crustaceans along the bank of the Matla River at Port Canning. Rec. Indian Mus. 34:289-298.

1932b. Freezing points of bloods of certain littoral and estuarine animals. Carnegie Inst. Washington Publ. 435:93-102.

1932c. Observations on the parasites and commensals found associated with crustaceans and fishes at Dry Tortugas, Florida. *Ibid.* 435:103-115.

1932d. Inhabitants of certain sponges at Dry Tortugas. *Ibid.* 435:117-124.

1932e. Animals in brackish water ponds and pools at Dry Tortugas. *Ibid.* 435: 125-142.

1932f. Parasites of Japanese salamanders. Ecology 13:135-152.
1933. The gobies at Paknam. J. Siam Soc. Nat. Hist. Suppl. 9:173-178.
1933a. Parasites of Siamese fishes and crustaceans. J. Siam. Soc. Nat. Hist. Suppl. 9:179-191.
1934. Ecological segregation. Science 79:167-172.
1936. The migrations of animals from sea to land. Durham, N. C., x + 176.

Pearse, A. S. *et al.*
1935. The cenotes of Yucatan. Carnegie Inst. Washington Publ. 457:1-268.
1938. Fauna of the caves of Yucatan. Carnegie Inst. Wash. Publ. 491:iii + 304.

Pearse, A. S., & Hall, F. G.
1928. Homoiothermism, the origin of warm-blooded vertebrates. New York, ix + 119.

Pearse, A. S., Humm, H. J., & Wharton, G. W.
1942. Ecology of sand beaches at Beaufort, N. C. Ecol. Monogr. 12:35-190.

Peirce, G. J.
1901. Normal respiration and intramolecular respiration. Amer. Nat. 35:463-478.

Pelseneer, P.
1906. L'origine des faunes d'eau douce. Revue du mois, Paris 2:413-425.

Percival, E.
1929. A report on the fauna of the estuaries of the River Tamar and the River Lynher. J. Mar. Biol. Assn. United K. 16:81-108.

Perez, C.
1925. Sur le complexe éthologique du *Phascolion strombi*. Bull. soc. zool. Paris 50:74-76.
1928. Notes sur les epicardes et les rhizocéphales des côtes de France. Bull. Soc. Zool. France 53:523-528.

Perkins, R. C. L.
1897. Notes on some Hawaiian insects. Proc. Cambr. Philos. Soc. 9:373-380.

Perwitzschky, R.
1927. Untersuchungen unter normalen Aussenbedingungen und bei normaler Atemgrösse am ruhenden Menschen. Arch. Ohren. Nasen u. Kehlkopfheilk. 177:1-36.

Petersen, C. G., & Jensen, P. B.
1911. Valuation of the sea. I. Animal life on the sea bottom, its food and quantity. Danish Biol. Sta. Rept. 20:3-81.

Petit, M. G.
1921. Observations sur certains Poissons de Madagascar présentant une adaptation a la locomotion terrestre. Bull. Mus. (1921):216-220.
1922. Les Périophthalmes, Poissons fouisseurs. Bull. Mus. Nat. Hist. Nat. 28: 404-408.

Pflüger, E.
1875. Ueber die physiologische Verbrennung in den lebendigen Organismen. Arch. ges. Physiol. 10:251-367.

Phillips, A. H.
1922. Analytical search for metals in Tortugas marine organisms. Pap. Tortugas Lab. Carnegie Inst. Washington 18:95-99.

Pickel, F. W.
1899. The accessory bladders of the Testudinata. Amer. Nat. 2:291-301.

Pierron, R. P., & Huang, Y. C.
1926. Animal succession on denuded rocks. Publ. Puget Sound Biol. Sta. 5:149-157.

Pike, F. H.
1923a. Adaptation considered as a special case under the theorem of le Chateleir. Ecology 4:129-134.
1924. On the difficulties encountered in the evolution of air-breathing vertebrates. Science 59:402-403.
1928. A further note on the difficulties encountered by land vertebrates in their development. Science 68:378-379.
1929. The driving force in organic evolution and a theory of the origin of life. Ecology 10:167-176.

Pike, F. H., & Scott, E. L.
1915. The significance of certain internal conditions of the organism in organic evolution. Amer. Nat. 49:321-359.

Plate, L.
1932. Vererbungslehre, mit besonderer Berücksichtigung der Abstammungslehre und des Menschen. I. Mendelismus. Jena, x + 554.

Plimmer, V. G., & R. H. A.
1922. Vitamins and the choice of food. London, xii + 164.

Poisson, R., & Remy, P.
1925. Contribution à l'étude de la faune des eau saumâtres. I. Le canal de Caen à la mer. Bull. Soc. Linn. Normandie 8:144-155.

Potter, G. E.
1927. Respiratory function of the swim bladder in Lepidosteus. J. Exper. Zool. 49:45-67.

Poulton, E. B.
1908. Essays on evolution; 1889-1907. Oxford, xlvii + 479.

Powers, E. B.
1921. Experiments and observations on the behavior of marine fishes towards the hydrogen-ion concentration of the sea water in relation to their migrating movements and habitat. Publ. Puget Sound Biol. Sta. 3:1-22.
1921. The physiology of the respiration of fishes in relation to the hydrogen-ion concentration of the medium. J. Gen. Physiol. 4:305-317.
1922. The alkaline reserve of the blood of fish in relation to the environment. Amer. J. Physiol. 61:380-383.
1923. The absorption of oxygen by the herring as affected by the CO_2 tension of the sea water. Ecology 4:307-312.
1927. The behavior of sea-water, lake-water, and bog-water at different carbon dioxide tensions. Prog. Ecol. Soc. Amer. (1927):13-14.

1927a. A simple colorimetric method for field determinations of the carbon dioxide tension and free carbon dioxide, bicarbonates and carbonates in solution in natural waters. I. A theoretical discussion. Ecology 8:333-338.

1930. The relation between pH and aquatic animals. Amer. Nat. 64:342-366.

Powers, E. B. *et al.*

1932. The relation of respiration of fishes to environment. Ecol. Monogr. 2:385-473.

Powers, E. B., & Logan, G. A.

1925. The alkaline reserve of the blood plasma of the viviparous perch (*Cymatogaster aggregatus* Gib.) in relation to carbon dioxide tension, the oxygen tension, and the alkalinity of sea water. Publ. Puget Sound Biol. Sta. 3:337-360.

Powers, E. B., & Shipe, L. M.

1928. The rate of oxygen absorption by certain marine fishes as affected by the oxygen content and carbon dioxide tension of sea water. Publ. Puget Sound Biol. Sta. 5:365-372.

Prenant, M.

1929. Remarque sur les conditions écologique dans les estuaires. Bull. Soc. Zool. France 54:210-212.

Prenant, M., & Teissier, G.

1924. Note ethiologique sur la fauna marine de Roscoff. Trav. Station Biol. Roscoff Paris, 2 (1924):1-49).

Price, W. A., & Gunter, G.

1943. Certain recent geological and biological changes in South Texas, with consideration of probable causes. Trans. Texas Acad. Sci. 26:138-156.

Pruthi, H. S.

1927a. The ability of fishes to extract oxygen at different hydrogen-ion concentrations of the medium. J. Mar. Biol. Assn. U. K. 14:741-747.

1927. Preliminary observations on the relative importance of the various factors responsible for the death of fishes in polluted waters. *Ibid.* 14:729-739.

1927b. The influence of some physical and chemical conditions of water on may-fly larvae (*Choëon dipterum* L.). Bull. Entomol. Res. 17:279-284.

1933. Seasonal changes in the physical and chemical conditions of the water of the tank in the Indian Museum compound. Internat. Rev. Ges. Hydrobiol. 28:46-67.

Pryde, J.

1931. Recent advances in biochemistry. Philadelphia, x + 393.

Przylecki, St. J.

1926. La dégradation de l'acide urique chez les vertébrés. 3. Reparation de l'uricase et de l'allanotoinase ches vertébrés poikilothermes. Arch. Internat. Physiol. 26:33-53.

Pütter, A.

1907. Die Ernährung der Wassertiere. Zs. allg. Physiol. 7:283-320.

1909. Die Ernährung der Fische. Zeitschr. allg. Physiol. 9:147-242.

Pyefinch, K. A.
1943. The intertidal ecology of Beardsey Island, North Wales, with special reference to the recolonization of rock surfaces, and the rock-pool environment. J. Animal. Ecol. 12:82-108.

Quigley, J. P.
1928. Reactions of an elasmobranch (*Squalus sucklii*) to variations in the salinity of the surrounding medium. Biol. Bull. 54:165-190.

Raben, K. von
1934. Veränderungen im Kiemendeckel und in den Kiemen einiger Brachyuren (Decapoden) im Verlauf der Anpassung an die Feuchtluftatmung. Zeitschr. wiss. Zool. A145:425-461.

Raffy, Anne
1931. Respiration cutanée de larvaes d'hydrophiles. Compt. Rend. Soc. Biol. 106:900-901.
1932. Variations de la consommation d'oxygène dessous au cours de la mort de Poissons marins sténoulins passant de l'eau de mer à l'eau douce. Compt. Rend. Acad. Sci. Paris 194:1522-1524.

Rasmussen, A. T. & G. B.
1917. The volume of the blood during hibernation and other periods of the year in the woodchuck (*Marmota monax*). Am. J. Physiol. 44:132-148.

Rauther, M.
1910. Die accessorischen Atmungsorgane der Knochenfische. Erg. u. Fortschr. d. Zool. 2:517-585.

Redeke, H. C.
1922. Zur Biologie der Niederlandischen Brackwasser typen. Bijdr. Dierk, Amsterdam (Feest-Num., M. Weber):329-335.

Rees, Gwendolen
1941. The resistance of the flatworm, *Monocelis fusca,* to changes in temperature and salinity under natural and experimental conditions. J. Animal Ecol. 10:121-145.

Reese, A. M.
1932. Life of West Virginia caves. Anat. Rec. 54:110.

Regan, C. T.
1924. Mendelism and evolution. Nature 113:569.

Reibisch, J.
1926. Über Änderung in der Fauna der Kieler Bucht. Schrift. Naturwiss. Ver. Schleswig-Holstein 17:227-232.

Reid, D. M.
1930. Salinity interchange between sea-water in sand and overflowing freshwater at low tide. J. Mar. Biol. Assn. U. K. 16:609-614.
1932. Salinity interchange between salt water in sand and overflowing freshwater at low tide. II. *Ibid.* 17:299-306.

Remane, A.
1929. Gastrotricha. Kükenthal's Handb. Zool. 2:121-186.

Rice, L.
1930. Peculiarities in the distribution of barnacles in communities and their causes. Publ. Puget Sound Biol. Sta. 7:249-257.

Richard, J.
1900. Essai sur les crustacés considérés dans leurs rapports avec l'hygiène, la médecine, et al parasitologie. Lille, 1-83.
1899. Essai sur les Parasites et les commensaux des Crustacés. Arch. Parasitol. 2:548-595.

Richards, H. G.
1929. Freshwater snails in brackish water. Nautilus 42:129-130.
1929a. The resistance of the freshwater snail, *Physa heterostropha* (Say), to sea water. Biol. Bull. 57:292-299.

Richards, O. W., & Robson, G. C.
1926. The species problem and evolution. Nature 117:345-347, 382-384.

Richardson, H.
1928. Life and sea water. *Ibid.* 122:682-683.

Richet, C. et O.
1926. De l'accoutumance des poissons marins aux eaux sursaturées. C. R. Acad. Sci. Paris 183:627-628.

Richet, C., Bachrach, E., & Cardot, H.
1928. De l'adaptation des animaux marin à la mise à sec. C. R. Acad. Sci. Paris 187:862-865.

Rigg, G. B., Thompson, T. G., Lorah, J. R., & Williams, K. T.
1927. Dissolved gases in waters of some Puget Sound bogs. Bot. Gaz. 84:264-278.

Ritchie, A. D.
1927. Lactic acid in fish and crustacean muscle. Brit. J. Exper. Biol. 4:322-332.

Robertson, C.
1906. Ecological adaptation and ecological selection. Science 23:307-310.

Robertson, T. B.
1923. The chemical basis of growth and senescence. New York, viii + 389.

Robinson, W.
1928. Water binding capacity of colloids a definite factor in winter hardiness of insects. J. Econ. Entomol. 20:80-88.

Robson, G. C.
1925. The animal life of estuaries. J. Quekett Micros. C. London, 15:161-168.
1928. The species problem. London, vii + 283.

Rogers, C. G.
1927. Textbook of comparative physiology. New York, xvi + 635.
1928. Physiological evidence of evolution and animal relationship. Sci. Mo. 27: 506-521.

Rogers, F. T.
1920. The relation of the cerebral hemispheres to arterial blood pressure and body temperature regulation. Arch. Neurol. and Psychiatry 4:148-150.

Romer, A. S.
1945. Vertebrate paleontology. Chicago ix + 687.

Roughley, T. C.
1947. Wonders of the great barrier reef. N. Y. xiii + 282.

Rountree, L. G.
1922. The water balance of the body. Physiol. Rev. 2:116-169.

Rubner, M.
1924. Aus dem Leben des Kaltblüters. I. Teil: Die Fische. Biochem. Zeitschr. 148:222-267.
1924a. Aus der Leben des Kaltblüters. II. Teil: Amphibien und Reptilien. *Ibid.* 148:268-307.
1924b. Ueber die Bildung der Körpermesse in Tierreich und die Beziehung der Masse zum Energie-verbrauch. Sitz. Ber. Ak. Wis. Berlin (1924):217-234.

Russell, F. S., & Yonge, C. M.
1928. The seas. London, xiii + 379.

Salisbury, E. J.
1922. Stratification and hydrogen-ion concentration of the soil in relation to leaching and plant succession with special reference to woodlands. J. Ecol. 9:220-240.

Saunders, J. T.
1923. The measurement of the carbon dioxide output of fresh-water animals by means of indicators. P. Cambridge Philos. Soc. 1:43-48.

Saunders, L. G.
1928. Some marine insects of the Pacific coast of Canada. Ann. Ent. Soc. America 21:521-545.

Scharff, R. F.
1926. Sur le problème de l'ile de Krakatua. C. R. Assoc. Franç. Avanc. Sci. 49: 746-750.

Schechter, V.
1943. Tolerance of the snail, *Thais floridana,* to waters of low salinity and the effect of size. Ecology 24:493-499.

Schiller, F. C. S.
1924. Tantalus or the future of man. New York, vii + 66.

Schliënz, W.
1923. Verbreitung und Verbreitungs-bedingungen der höherer Krebse im Mündungsgebiet der Elbe. Arch. Hydrobiol. 14:429-452.

Schlieper, C.
1928. Die biologische Bedeutung der Salzkonzentration der Gewässer. Naturwiss. 16:229-237.
1929. Die Osmoregulation der Süsswasserkrebse. Zool. Anzeig. (1929):214-218.
1929a. Über die Einwirkung Niederer Salzkonzentrationen auf marine Organismen. Zeit. f. vergl. Physiol. 9:478-514.
1930. Die Osmoregulation wasserlebenden Tiere. Biol. Rev. 5:309-356.

1933. Die Brackwassertiere und ihre Lebensbedingungen vom physiologischen Standpunkt aus betrachtet. Verhandl. d. Internat. Verein. f. theor. u. angewan. Limnologie 6:113-146.

Schweitz, J., & Darteville, E.

1948. Sur l'origine des mollusques thallassoides du lac Tanganika. Inst. Roy. Colon. Belge, Mem. 16(7):1-58.

Schöttle, Elfriede

1931. Morphologie und Physiologie der Atmung bei wasserschlamm- und landlebenden Gobiiformes. Zeitschr. wiss. Zool. 140:1-114.

Schreitmuller, W., & Relinghaus, H.

1926. Untersuchungen am lebenden Auge sowie Bemerkungen über die Lebensweise des indischen Kletterfisches (*Anabas scandens* Dold.). Arch. Naturges. 91:109-129.

Schulz, F. N.

1923. Blutgewinnung und Untersuchungung des Blutes im allgemein. Crustaceen, Tracheaten. Winterstein's Hanb. vergl. Physiol. 1:669-812.

Schwabe, E.

1933. Über die Osmoregulation verschiedener Krebse (Malacostracen). Zeitschr. vergl. Physiol. 19:185-236.

Sciacchitano, I.

1927. Ancora sull'-*Artemia salina* delle saline de Cagliari. Riv. Biologia 9:79-86.

Scott, G. G.

1910. Effects of changes in the density of water upon the blood of fishes. Bull. U. S. Bureau Fisheries 28:1143-1150.

1916. The evolutionary significance of the osmotic pressure of the blood. Am. Nat. 50:641-663.

Scott, W.

1910. The fauna of a solution pond. Proc. Indiana Acad. Sci. (1910):1-48.

Seiwell, H. R.

1931. Observations on the ammonia content of sea water. Ecology 12:485-488.

Semper, K.

1878. Ueber die Lunge von *Birgus latro*. Zeitschr. wiss. zool. 30:282-287.

Setchell, W. A.

1928. Coral reefs as zonal plant formations. Science 68:119-121.

Seurat, L. G.

1926. L'estuaire de l'Akarit (Golfe de Gabès). Bull. Soc. Hist. Afrique Nord 18:80-82.

Shelford, V. E.

1929. Laboratory and field ecology. Baltimore, xii + 608.

Shelford, V. E., & Powers, E. B.

1915. An experimental study of the movements of herring and other marine fishes. Biol. Bull. 28:315-334.

Sherff, E. E.

1912. The vegetation of Shokie Marsh, with special reference to subterranean organs and their interrelationships. Bot. Gaz. 53:415-435.

Shoup, C. S.

1932. Salinity of the medium and its effects on respiration in the sea-anemone. Ecology 13:81-85.

Simroth, H.

1891. Die Entstehung der Landtiere. Leipzig, viii + 492.

Slonaker, J. R.

1926. Long fluctuations in voluntary activity of the albiano rat. Amer. J. Physiol. 77:503-508.

Smith, H. M.

1927. Some fresh-water fishes of Siam. T. Amer. Fisheries Soc. 56:213-226.

Smith, H. W.

1930. Lung-fish. Sci. Mo. 31:467-470.

1930a. Metabolism of the lung-fish, *Protopterus aethiopicus*. J. Biol. Chem. 88: 97-129.

1931. Observations on the African lung-fish, *Protopterus aethiopicus*, and on evolution from water to land environments. Ecology 12:164-181.

1933. The functional and structural evolution of the vertebrate kidney. Sigma Xi Quar. 21:141-151.

Snoke, A. M.

1929. The determination of dissolved oxygen with the micro-Winkler apparatus of Thompson and Miller. Ecology 10:163-164.

Snyder, C.

1909. The physical conditions at the beginnings of life. Sci. Progr. 3:579-596.

1911. Life without oxygen, the anaerobic beginnings of life. *Ibid*. 6:107-134.

Spencer, W. P.

1929. Day and night periodicity in four species of freshwater fishes. Anat. Rec. 44:197.

Spengel, J. W.

1904. Schwimmblasen, lungen und Kiementaschen. Zool. Jahrb. Suppl. 7:727-749.

Splendore, A.

1918. Studi nell' interesse di una lotta biologica contro le arvicole. Bollet. Ser. B., Ministerio di Agricottura, Rome.

Steen, W. B.

1929. On the permeability of the frog's bladder to water. Anat. Rec. 43:215-220.

Stefani, I. de

1929. La faune insulare. L'Universo 10:393-416.

Stephen, A. C.

1930. Studies on the Scottish marine fauna: the fauna of the sandy and muddy areas of the tidal zone. Trans. Roy. Soc. Edinburgh 56:291-306.

1930a. Additional observations on the fauna of the sandy and muddy areas of the tidal zone. *Ibid*. 56:521-535.

Stephenson, T. A.

1942. Causes of intertidal zonation. Nature 150:158.

Stephenson, T. A., Stephenson, Anne, Tandy, G., & Spender, M.
1931. The structure and ecology of low isles and other reefs. Great Barrier Reef Exped. 1928-29 Sci. Repts. 3:17-112.

Stevens, B. A.
1929. Ecological observations on Callianassidae of Puget Sound. Ecology 10:399-405.

Stolte, H. A.
1928. Die Cupula in Labyrinth der Fische im lebenden und fixierten Zustande. Zool. Anz. 77:176-184.

Stowell, F. P.
1927. The adsorption of ions from sea water by sand. J. Marine Biol. Assn. 14:955-956.

Stunkard, H. W., & Shaw, R. C.
1931. The effect of dilution of sea water on the activity and longevity of certain marine cercariae. Biol. Bull. 61:242-271.

Sumner, F. B.
1906. The physiological effects upon fishes of changes in the density and salinity of water. Bull. U. S. Bu. Fish. 25:53-108.
1911. Fundulus and fresh water. Science, U. S. 34:928-931.
1928. Observations on the influence of a multifactor color variation in white-footed mice (Peromyscus). Amer. Nat. 62:193-206.
1929. Is evolution a continuous or discontinuous process? Sci. Mo. 29:72-78.
1929a. The analysis of a concrete case of intergradation between two subspecies. P. Nat. Acad. Sci. 15:110-120, 481-493.
1932. Genetic, distributional, and evolutionary studies of deer mice (Peromyscus). Bibliogr. Genet. 9:1-106.

Sumner, F. B., Osburn, R. C., & Cole, L. J.
1913. A biological survey of the waters of Woods Hole and vicinity. I. Physical and zoological. Bull. U. S. Bur. Fisheries 31:1-442.

Sverdrup, H. V., Johnson, M. W., & Fleming, R. H.
1942. The oceans, their physics, chemistry, and general biology. N. Y. x + 1087.

Szalay, L.
1928. A viziatakák ellenállóképessege. Ann. Hist. Nat. Mus. Nation. Hungarici 25:427-438.

Tait, J.
1917. Experiments and observations on Crustacea. Part I. Immersion experiments on Ligia. P. Roy. Soc. Edinburgh 37:50-58.

Taylor, H. F.
1922. Deductions concerning the air bladder and the specific gravity of fishes. Bull. U. S. Bur. Fisheries 38:121-126.
1932. Resources of the ocean. J. Franklin Inst. 214:167-196.

Thienemann, A.
1926. Dipteren aus den Salzegewässern von Oldesloe. Mitteil. Geogr. Ges. u. Naturhist. Mus. Lübeck. 31:102-126.

Thompson, T. G., & Miller, R. C.
1928. Apparatus for the micro-determination of dissolved oxygen. Ind. Eng. Chem. 20:774.
1927. Improved methods for the determination of dissolved oxygen and hydrogen-ion concentration. Progr. Ecol. Soc. Amer. (1927):7.

Thompson, T. G., Miller, R. C., Hitchins, G. H., & Todd, S. P.
1927. A study of the hourly changes in the condition of the sea water off Puget Sound Biological Station, during one complete tidal cycle. Progr. Ecol. Soc. Amer. (1927):7.

Thompson, W. F. and J. B.
1919. The spawning of the grunion, *Leuresthes tenuis.* State California Fish. Bull. 3:1-29.

Thomson, J. A.
1922. The haunts of life. New York, xv + 272.

Thorpe, W. H.
1927. The fauna of the brackish pools of the Sussex Coast. Trans. S. E. Union Scien. Soc. (1927):27-34.
1927a. Report on the brackish water insects. T. Zool. Soc. London 75: 447-449.
1930. The biology of the petroleum fly (*Psilopa petrolii,* Cog.). T. Entomol. Soc. London 78:331-343.
1931. The biology of the petroleum fly. Science 73:101-103.
1932. Colonization of the sea by insects. Nature 130:629.
1931. Miscellaneous records of insects inhabiting the saline waters of Californian desert regions. Pan-Pacific Ent. 7:145-153.

Thorson, T., & Svihla, A.
1943. Correlation of the habitats of amphibians with their ability to survive the loss of body water. Ecology 24:374-381.

Tillyard, R. J.
1917. The biology of dragonflies. Cambridge, xii + 396.

Tokunaga, M.
1930. The morphological and biological studies on a new marine crane-fly, *Limonia* (*Dicranomyia*) *monostromia,* Japan. Mem. Col. Agr. Kyoto Imp. Univ. 10:1-193.

True, R. H.
1915. The calculation of total salt content and of specific gravity in marine waters. Science 42:732-735.

Vaughan, T. W.
1919. Corals and the formation of coral reefs. Smithsonian Rept. (1917):189-276.

Vernon, H. M.
1899. The death temperature of certain marine organisms. J. Physiol. 25:131-136.

Verwey, J.
1927. Einiges aus der Biologie von *Talitrus saltator* (Mont.) Congrès Internation. 10e Zool. Budapest (1927) 2:1156-1162.
1930. Einiges über die Biologie Ost-Indinischer Mangrove-krabben. Treubia 12: 167-261.

Vestal, A. G.
1914. Internal relations of terrestrial associations. Amer. Nat. 48:413-445.

Viets, K.
1926. Mitteilung über das Vorkommen von Halacariden in der Kiemenhöle des Flusskrebses. Verhandl. Internat. Verein. theor. u. angewand. Limnol. 3:460-473.
1927. *Atractides spongicolus* n. sp., eine Hydracarine aus einem Süsswasserschwamm von Celebes. Zool. Anz. 71:109-112.
1928. Note on British freshwater Halacaridae. J. Queckett Micr. Club 16:71-74.

Vogel, R.
1927. Über drei an Salzwasser angepasste Insektengattungen an der östlichen Mittelmeerküste. Internat. Rev. Hydrobiol. and Hydrogr. 17:355-356.

Viosca, P.
1931. Spontaneous combustion in the marshes of Southern Louisiana. Ecology 12:439-442.

Ward, H. B.
1910. Internal parasites of the Sebago salmon. Bull. U. S. Bur. Fisheries 28: 1151-1194.

Wardlaw, H. S. H.
1931. Some aspects of the adaptation of living organisms to their environment. Rept. Smithsonian Inst. (1931):389-411.

Warming, E.
1909. Oecology of plants. Oxford, xi + 422.

Watson, J. G.
1928. Mangrove forests of the Malay Peninsula. Malayan For. Rec. 6:1-275.

Weaver, J. E., & Clements, F. E.
1929. Plant Ecology. New York, xx + 520.

Weber, M.
1890-1897. Zoologische Ergebnisse einer Reise in Niederländisch Ost-Indien. Leiden 4 bde.

Webster, H. E., & Benedict, J. E.
1884. The Annelida Chaetopoda from Provincetown and Wellfleet, Massachusetts. Rept. U. S. Com. Fish. (1881):699-747.

Weese, A. O.
1928. The Ecological Society of America, Program of the meeting at New York. Bull. Ecol. Soc. Amer. 9:1-16.

Weiss, Chas. M.
1948. The seasonal occurrence of sedentary marine organisms in Biscayne Bay, Florida. Ecology 29:133-145.

Wells, M. M.
1915. The reactions and resistance of fishes in their natural environment to salts. J. Exper. Zool. 19:243-283.

Wells, R. C.
1922. Carbon-dioxide content of sea water at Tortugas. Pap. Tortugas Lab. Carnegie Inst. Washington 18:87-93.

Weve, H.

1922. Der Lichtsinn von *Periophthalmus koebreuteri.* Arch. f. vergl. Ophthalmologie 3:265-278.

Wheeler, W. M.

1910. Ants, their structure, development and behavior. New York, xxv + 663.

White, W. E.

1930. Notes on a fresh-water medusa found in Stallworth Lake, Tuscaloosa, Alabama. Biol. Bull. 59:222-232.

Wigglesworth, V. B.

1933. The effect of salts on the anal gills of the mosquito larva. J. Exper. Biol. 10:1-15.

1933a. The function of the anal gills of the mosquito larva. *Ibid.* 10:16-26.

1933b. Adaptation of mosquito larvae to salt water. *Ibid.* 10:27-37.

Willem, V.

1920. Observations sur la respiration des amphibièns. Bruxelles Bull. Acad. Roy. (1920):299-314, 339-347.

Willmer, E. N.

1934. Observations on the respiration of certain tropical freshwater fishes. J. Exper. Biol. 11:283-306.

Wilson, C. B.

1913. Crustacean parasites of West Indian fishes and land crabs, with descriptions of new species. Proc. U. S. Nat. Mus. 44:189-277.

Wilson, F. C.

1920. Description of an apparatus for obtaining samples of water at different depths for bacteriological analysis. J. Bact. 5:103-108.

Wodsedalek, J. E.

1912. Life history and habits of *Trogoderma tarsale* (Melsh.), a museum pest. Ann. Entomol. Soc. Amer. 5:367-382.

1917. Five years of starvation of larvae. Science 46:366.

Worley, L. G.

1929. The marine rotifer *Brachionus mulleri* subjected to salinity changes. Ecology 10:420-426.

Wornichin, N. N.

1926. Zur biologie der bittersalzigen Seen in der Umgebung von Pjatigorsk (nördl. Kaukasus). Arch Hydrobiol. 17:628-643.

Wright, A. H.

1931. Life histories of the frogs of Okefinokee Swamp, Georgia. New York, xv + 497.

Young, R. T.

1941. The distribution of the mussel (*Mytilus californianus*) in relation to the salinity of its environment. Ecology 22:378-386.

Zernov, S. A.

1909. Grundzüge der Verbreitung der Tierwelt des Schwartzen Meeres bei Sebastopol. I. Benthos. Internat. Rev. Hydrobiol. 2:99-123.

Zobell, C. E., & Feltham, C. B.
1938. Bacteria as food for certain marine invertebrates. Jour. of Marine Research 1:312-327.

Zoond, A., & Charles, E.
1931. Studies on the localization of respiratory exchange in invertebrates. I. The respiratory mechanism of the freshwater crab Potamonautes. J. Exper. Biol. 8:250-257.

INDEX

Type Faces Used in This Book

Text—Cloister

Headings—Metromedium

Incidental—Metrothin and Tempo

Binding

Holliston Rovite Linen
(washable, vermin-proof)